The Fakir

Dear Anita,
   May the blessings
of your Guru and God
always be bestowed
upon you.

Lots of love,
Rajishree.
Mumbai
18-7-13.

THE FAKIR

First FULL CIRCLE Paperback Edition, August 2010
First Reprint, 2010
Second Reprint, 2011
Third Reprint, 2012
Fourth Reprint, 2012
Fifth Reprint, 2013

ISBN 978-81-7621-197-0

Cover Design by Ms. Poonam Bevli Sahi, FACET

Designed by ISHTIHAAR

Published by arrangement with the author

Published by **FULL CIRCLE** *PUBLISHING*
J-40, Jorbagh Lane, New Delhi-110003
Tel: 24620063, 24621011 • Fax: 24645795
E-mail: contact@fullcirclebooks.in • *website:* www.fullcirclebooks.in

Printed at Rakesh Press, A-22, Sector-68, Noida-201301

PRINTED IN INDIA

10/15/05/06/20/ISHTIHAAR/CP/RP/RP/OP225/NP250

The Fakir

Ruzbeh N. Bharucha

To Sai Baba
of Shirdi,
all the Perfect
Masters and
The Universal
Mother
- Ruzbeh N Bharucha

THE SMALL BOY, with curly ruffled hair, a twinkle in his eyes and dimples on his cheeks, whispered, "Dah-ddy, please don't go!".

The young girl, with hair like gold but eyes hard and accusing, spat out in a tone that felt as though she was walking on his grave, "You're a pathetic loser, dad".

Just as a million times before, he woke up with a start and his tired eyes looked towards the old alarm clock. He winced, his stomach hurt and he cursed. It wasn't even three. He had barely slept for half an hour. He shut his eyes, breathed-in deep and prayed for sleep. He hadn't slept well for a long time. Too long a time – and he didn't want to stay awake, yet another night.

The room was illuminated by a candle, which silently caressed the darkness with a golden yellow glow. According to him, fire dispelled darkness and invited noble spirits (he even called them Guardian Angels) and most importantly, kept unwanted spirits (he called them astral bums) out. But thoughts were within, and only the flame of peace could dispel the chaos raging in his mind. Where peace was concerned, major bankruptcy issues prevailed.

He was thirsty, as usual. The whisky either wasn't as good as it claimed to be or he had drunk more than usual. With eyes shut, he tried to ascertain the quantum, he had like a thirsty fish consumed, the previous day. He had started rather early. Too early even for him, around noon. Then, after an hour or so of filling himself up with the 'earthly spirit', he had gone for his usual seven-mile walk. With his flask, of course, and then kept drinking till...hmm... whatever.

The man moaned out loud, as though, trying to plead with his mind to shut up and focus on sleep.

Seconds later, he *did* sleep.

HE KNEW HE had to be on the move once again. He did not have much choice in the matter. The dreams and the nightmares were relentless in their one point agenda; to ravage his last vestiges of sanity. For years, he had lived like a gypsy, never surviving a place for more than a few months. Eleven months, being an all-time record. Of course, that was largely due to the fact that he lay horizontal, on a hospital bed, for three months, undergoing tests for an illness no one could diagnose and thus, inevitably, no one could cure.

It took him a day to settle all the bills and repack his meagre belongings. Packed so often, that he could do it perfectly well, even half asleep, or completely drunk, absolutely far away from reality. He was considered a gypsy and a hippie but the only thing he really longed for were roots, but that, he knew, was not in his karma; at least not in the karma of this lifetime.

He had no friends. No one, but the landlord, even knew his complete name. He would be missed by the street urchins who he gave money and food to and by the staff of the few restaurants he once in a while visited; to either restore his sanity with human company or just eat food that was not out of some can. Yes, he would be missed most by the old turbaned Sikh, who sold him liquor and spoke about his childhood spent in the fields of a small village near Amritsar, half an hour away from the holy Golden Temple. The old man would cry when drunk, which he was often, and narrate incidents about his childhood, his village, his family; but mainly, cry at not being able to leave the city where he had lived for the past sixty years and return 'home'.

"Why don't you go back then?"

"Go back to what? All is gone. What will I survive on? Who will take care of me if I fall ill? No my son, I can't go... should have gone forty years ago but kept telling myself, will go later, will go later, and now it's too late. Should have gone earlier. Really should have. Now, it's too late. Am too old and it won't be the same. My soul's there but unfortunately my body has to remain here, in this mother-freaking city with no heart. Why didn't I leave when I could have? I was an idiot. All my life I longed for my village, which I could have easily gone to, if I hadn't been such a confused greedy fool."

The young man would nod and when he himself was drunk, would once in a way, reply.

"Yeah, I know what you mean. When the heart and soul want to be someplace else, but the body for whatever reason has to stay away, that's hell. One does not need to die to experience hell. Most often, hell is just a state of mind."

Either do what your soul really desires and if you can't, for whatever reason, then make peace with yourself and accept your present situation, with grace, as the will of the Lord. There is no other way son....

Then, a small voice would whisper in his raging heart, 'Son, then change your state of mind; either do what your soul really desires and if you can't, for whatever reason, then make peace with yourself and accept your present situation, with grace, as the will of the Lord. There is no other way son....'

And he knew the small voice within him spoke the words of Ancient Truth, but he ignored it. Either he was too angry, or weak or just not ready to accept and embrace the only sane path that would allow him to breathe in peace and exhale with his sanity intact. It takes wisdom to give life one's best shot and then accept gracefully whatever fate or providence has in store, with total positive surrender.

HE KNEW HE would have to begin work once again. He had saved enough to last him for over two years. Now he had a few months left to live life the way he was accustomed to. Then, be part of civilization or better still, mix a few tablets in his favourite malt whisky and wish the world a figgin good-bye and enter la-la land.

He knew the second alternative was the ideal one but he wasn't going to give his detractors such a juicy excuse to further crucify him. If he were dead and gone and holding a harp in one hand and a stiff drink in the other and with wings attached to his ass, that would convince his kids, once and for all, that a certain section of the world was right and that he had really deserted them, when the reality was something so very different.

Hmm? So what's it gonna be? Obnoxious life or grand release? Hmm? Na! Get on with existing, if not for anything, then to stick out like a sore thumb to the world, part of which wanted him to stop taking up space and air. He wasn't going to give them any such joy and he was going to live for his kids... Even though, his daughter hated him and his son, in all probability, thought, he had walked out on him.

"Rudra, you are buggered, old chap." Saying this, he looked around the room, nodded, as though, thanking the spirits that inhabited the room with him, and smiled to the painting of Lord Ganesh...the podgy elephant-headed God, son of Lord Siva and Parvati... who so often, prevented him, from killing himself. He folded his hands, did a *namaste* to Lord Ganesh, picked up his two haversacks, turned around, sighed and left the rented room, never to return again.

HE KNEW THAT he had to constantly be in control of his emotions. He had to live in the moment, or else the memories of the past would drive him insane with grief and the cross that he carried, would bury him into the ground. He did not live in denial. He did not romanticize his pain and state of misery. He certainly did not visualize a happy ending. All he did, in order to remain sane, was to live in the moment. That meant, being present, in everything he did; thus when he was listening to music, he was totally immersed in music. When he ate food, his focus was on the food. When he went for his seven-mile walk everyday, he walked, observed, and was in the 'darn' moment. No thoughts. No aching for the past. No anxiety for the future. He remembered his eternal Master.

"Rudra, God is in the moment. He isn't in the past or the future. If you can't live in the moment, if you can't live as though that moment is your last, then you aren't living son, just existing. Live, as though, you aren't going to live again. Enjoy the experience, as though you aren't going to get an opportunity to enjoy it ever again. You are eating that juicy mango now. Eat, as though this is your last mango. Eat, as though never again you are going to put your teeth into that golden-orange pulp. Now feel the difference. You will never forget the taste. Now, how does it taste, son?"

"Delicious...but I would enjoy the mango ten times more, if you weren't standing on my foot, oh great Master."

Rudra smiled. His eyes welled up. He breathed in deep. Little had he realized then that this simple philosophy would keep him alive, would keep him sane, would prevent him from being filled with hate and negativity; especially against those he once considered his very own. He could not control his dreams but during the hours he was awake, being in the moment saved him from going mad with thoughts and memories. Most of all, being in the moment saved him from turning into somebody he himself would abhor.

Of course, he could no longer eat mangoes. Ironically, the day his Master had taught him how to enjoy and embrace the present moment, was also the last time he had eaten the king of fruits, so many years ago. How

It takes wisdom to give life one's best shot and then accept gracefully whatever fate or providence has in store, with total positive surrender.

many years ago? 'Seems another lifetime, but yeah, You are right Old Man, the taste still remains'.

THE BLACK VAN he drove was his link to the outside world. It allowed him to travel, whenever and wherever he wanted to; especially when the need to flee from a place and his own suicidal state of mind became overpowering. The van had witnessed his tears and anguish and often, taken on the role of a silent companion.

Often, when he was inside the van, he felt sheltered from storms, both within him and from the world outside. There were days when he withdrew inside the van, as though, withdrawing within himself and like a baby nourished within the womb, he too felt strengthened; strong enough to at least overpower the overwhelming urge to end his life.

The black van was once used as an ambulance. Either the nursing home that owned it did not know how to manage the sick or the small town, all of a sudden, became a healthy small town... too healthy for the nursing home's financial good. Whatever the reason, he bought it at a ridiculously low price.

He converted it into a mobile home, nothing fancy but with all the basic comforts of a house. He spent considerable time doing it up, for the simple reason that he did have all the time in the world. Of course, he was aware that this was not just a mere vehicle for transport, but a lifeline in more ways than one; his ship that could anchor anywhere and also set sail when the winds of depression threatened to smash him to pieces heartlessly.

In the womb of this black van, he spent days on mountaintops and nights in valleys or at the outskirts of some village or town, all tucked up, in bed, with either his books or seeing a good movie on his lap-top or just drinking and listening to music; alone but never really lonely. His Master was with him always. Rudra could feel His presence. His presence alone made the constant hell of living worth its while.

Rudra often realized that this black van of his, made of metal and innumerable nuts and bolts gave him more comfort, warmth and protection than many whom once he had considered his very own.

RUDRA KNEW HIS life was running out. He was well aware that he did not have much time. Before he died, he had to make his presence on planet earth worthwhile; and that was possible only by serving and helping those who needed a helping hand. ' I don't know how to go about doing this stuff Pa. I have no skills. I have no knowledge. Have no darn experience. Have no contacts. Have nothing but this pain that starts from my heart, passes my ass, reverses and then goes right through my skull. Just have pain Pa. Pain did no one, no good'. Then his Master's voice would echo, deep in the recesses of his heart and mind.

"You know son, pain is the greatest gift God could give his child, because it is pain that opens the door to compassion and love; and it is only compassion and love for all of creation that opens the doors of paradise and God consciousness. If you have been in pain, you understand and sympathize with the pain of others. It makes you more open to the peculiar behavior and weakness of others, as when in pain, you too have misbehaved or thought of misbehaving or hurting others or in a moment of weakness done things you shouldn't have. So you become less judgmental. More open. Pain makes you closer to all beings and God Himself. Pain makes you gentler and more humane to the tears and sorrow of others; and also allows you to appreciate good times, good people and real companionship. Pain of body, mind or heart, means the land is fertile for God to begin cultivating on your soul, my son. But if you let pain make you bitter, negative, mean, vindictive... Ah son, you have lost the greatest opportunity to walk in the shadow of God. But if you allow pain to harvest the good in you my child, then the kingdom of heaven is yours; not only when you exhale your last and leave your physical frame, but even when you live and with every breath you take while you live. The cross will remain, but your shoulders will get more strength. The whip will lash on your body but the balm of God will not allow pain to touch you. The kingdom of heaven is filled with wonders son; the greatest wonder of all, is to convert pain to God consciousness...wake up, Rudra, I know you are hearing me; don't you dare snore on me son...Rudra!"

HE DROVE THROUGH the open country, having left the city far behind. The black van passed fields (most often barren or too small for survival), mountains (could be hills too... whatever, very majestic), children (most often half naked, very often undernourished, as a rule extremely lively), accompanied by two-three gregarious dogs (who followed their young masters, with looks ranging from 'bored to hell, harrowed, or humans are potty'), livestock (undernourished cows, exhausted bullocks, nonchalant pigs, and extremely preoccupied birds), small towns (aping big cities) and smaller villages (that clung on to beautiful but dying traditions and ridiculous parochial prehistoric mindset with superstitions that only grew stronger by the decade) and a vast sky of various hues.

He listened to Neil Diamond and Leonard Cohen songs, and tried his vehicular best to avoid truck and bus drivers. He was convinced that the sole agenda of heavy vehicular drivers was to try their darn all to reduce the population of the country, by killing all those who were foolhardy enough to drive on the national highway.

But he never drove too fast. He was always of the opinion that the journey was as important as the destination and very often one spent more time on the journey than at the destination; thus it made more sense to enjoy the journey as much as is humanly possible.

He saw the truck driver try to overtake the car driving towards him, some twenty meters away. He was certain that all drivers involved were aware that this was a move that could be jotted down in vehicular history as either suicide, attempted murder or lock the truck driver away and melt down the key.

Rudra jammed hard on the brake and seconds later the truck managed to overtake the car and squeeze past his motionless van. If he had kept driving, he would have been dead. Hmm! That would have been the end of him! Hmm? Na. With his kind of luck, he would be alive but with the much needed limbs missing or perpetually out of action. Na!

Seconds later, with his van still motionless, Rudra saw the old man, lying in a pool of blood. For a few seconds he contemplated moving on and then sighed. He did not have an option any more, the soft voice had spoken within, and the decision made, without his consent. When he got out of his van, he noticed that though the traffic was heavy, nobody seemed to care about an old man lying in a pool of blood. That meant one of the two things: people drove either too fast or they were too preoccupied. He did not want to dwell on the third option; that people drove too fast, were too preoccupied and they did not care. (It applied to the way most people drove their lives too. Too fast, without enough thought and with so little compassion.)

Maybe they did care but they do not want to get involved, for whatever reason. In countries like the USA and in many parts of Europe, at least motorists would have phoned the authorities, describing the location of the accident and then driven away; certain that an ambulance or even a helicopter would be dashed off to the scene of tragedy. He had travelled through America, and witnessed the efficiency with which medical teams

God is in the moment. He isn't in the past or the future. If you can't live in the moment, if you can't live as though that moment is your last, then you aren't living son, just existing. Live, as though, you aren't going to live again. Enjoy the experience, as though you aren't going to get an opportunity to enjoy it ever again.

rushed to provide aid. They asked questions about insurance etc., later. First the aid was provided. If you then did not have the necessary papers or insurance, then of course you wished you had not survived. But the necessary help and medical provision were there at the earliest, with no questions asked.

In a developing country, especially in the interiors of the country, technology and communication as well as basic health care facilities were either non existent or pathetic. On highways, the Government did not provide necessary phones or help-lines and more importantly, even if the phone did exist, who could one call and even if one did know the number to dial for medical help, the call would not be made. Why? Simple! Nobody would come. Try it. In cities you might get lucky. Out in the country, you would need Divine Intervention, big time.

Maybe that is why those countries are called advanced. One could depend on a phone call; because human life has some value. We are big on culture and tradition and morality and clinging to history. You could cling on to ancient culture all you want to and one could trace one's heritage way into the ice age but if life does not hold value, then that culture and that heritage is worthless; it has failed; it is like a millstone around one's neck, while one tries to swim to the shore.

Maybe most countries in the West do not have an ancient culture or heritage. No past worth bragging about. But at least they have the present moment. They value individual life and the importance of improving the quality of life, be it for animal (man included) and all of nature. Valuing life is far more important than all that which has ever been achieved or procured; by man or God.

RUDRA GOT OUT of his van and slowly approached the old man. He was not certain of either his actions or intentions. He was following the soft voice within and he had learnt, sometimes in a very hard and painful manner and with disastrous consequences that the soft voice knew best, always.

The old man wore a white kaftan; a sort of a cotton robe, so similar to the one worn by Rudra's Master. He had a white cloth tied to his head, like an old-fashioned bandana and part of it was red and wet as blood oozed out from it. The old man lay on the side of the road, with his meagre belongings scattered around him. Rudra, for a few seconds, stood by the old man and though cars and trucks and the world moved by in varying degrees of speed, self-preservation and selfishness, he could hear nothing but the beat of his heart and the slow, deep intake and exhale of his own breath.

He knelt by the old man who lay in the fetal position. He softly touched the man's shoulder. Rudra could barely see the old man's face. Blood trickled down his white beard and the front of his robe was stained with dried blood. That meant two things. If blood still oozed from his forehead, in all probability life still lingered in the old veins. And if blood had begun to dry on his robe and even on his soft white beard, that also implied that he had lying on the road, bruised and left for dead for a long time.

Wow. In the land of sages, a fakir lay dying on the

road, mainly because nobody really had the time or courage or inclination to reach out a helping hand. Rudra felt for a pulse on the old man's cold but surprisingly strong wrist. He found the soothing beat of life and exhaled with relief. Then, all of a sudden cars began to halt and Rudra could hear footsteps from different directions.

"What happened?"

"Is he dead?"

"He looks like a Muslim sage..."

"He looks like Sai Baba of Shirdi..."

"What should we do?"

"You behave yourself or you too will be lying down near this poor old man, you rascal..."

Rudra still knelt near the old man, wondering what could be done. He was aware that there was no hospital near by. They were virtually between two cities, which very often in India meant, between two civilizations, while in between centuries of neglect and poverty existed. He turned and saw two families milling around him: seven adults, and two children. The elder child was visibly petrified. The other child, who had seconds earlier been addressed as 'a rascal' in all probability, Rudra concluded, would be an active cause of grief to his parents and to mankind in general.

"Where is the nearest hospital?" Rudra inquired.

"Two hours away. Did you see who did this?"

"No. He'll not make it if we don't do something now. We have to do something..."

"What if he dies on us?"

"We can't leave a man to die in the fear that he might die and we that have to go through some trouble..."

"What if he does die? Then what? The authorities just to make some quick money will harass the life out of us... Come on let's go."

Rudra breathed in deep. He did not blame them. He understood where their fears and insecurities sprang from and he was certain, that they would have helped and would have gone through all the trouble in the world to save this old man, but fear of a corrupt system, prevented them from stretching that extra mile. If the old man were to die, he would die, because of a system that harassed the innocent who wanted to be of service; caring souls who wanted to help. The old man would die because the cops and the hospital authorities would make life so miserable for the angels of mercy that the angels preferred to be human and turn a blind eye to misery and death itself; rather than be dragged into litigation, bribes and unending discomfort.

Rudra heard the cars start and then drive away. He exhaled and slowly picked up the old man in his arms. For some reason he wanted the old man to live. For many varied reasons; many of them selfish and personal. The old man did remind Rudra of his Master. His clothing, his appearance, his age; everything were so similar to Rudra's Old Man, his Master. That was the main reason. But another compelling motive was that by being near the old man, by being of some use to him,

Pain is the greatest gift God could give his child, because it is pain that opens the door to compassion and love; and it is only compassion and love for all of creation that opens the doors of paradise and God consciousness.

Rudra felt a certain sense of peace; as though his existence was of some use, some justification. Of course, another compelling reason to fight for this old man's life was that Rudra would not be able to live with another heartache; with another cross; with the guilt of not doing his darn all to save the old man. He carried the old man towards his van.

"Okay sweetheart, its you and me alone, and yeah God, lets hope you are awake and with us too. Come on old man, don't die on me, and wow, you do weigh something solid. You don't look so heavy but you weigh a ton man. Maybe it is your spirituality that is so heavy. Yeah. Now you lie on my soft bed and wow my backs friggin killing me. Okay now hold on while we make our calls." Rudra picked up his cell phone and then switched it on. There was no network; no signal.

"Global networking my sodding ass! Can't get a signal on a national highway. Shoot. Now what old man, it's freaking two hours to the hospital." He really was in a quandary. Should he attend to the old man's wounds himself or should he rush the old man to the hospital? Would the old man survive the long drive? "Will he survive your first aid Rudra? Wow. Should have listened to the family and become a doctor? Would have been of some use to somebody you messed up loser."

All of a sudden, Rudra nearly leapt out of his own skin; this was because the old man opened his eyes and seconds later managed a weak smile.

For a few moments, Rudra could do no more than stare at the old man. Though the bleeding continued, the old man showed neither the signs of pain, distress nor confusion. He looked at Rudra with so tender a gaze, that for the first time in years, all the pain, humiliation, allegations, heartache and the futility of existence not only seemed worthwhile but also made sense. Why; Rudra still was not very certain. What he was sure about, was that for the first time, his heart and more important, his very soul, seemed to accept with grace his past, present and future, with a surrender that not only was extremely comforting but absolutely shocking.

It was as though, if this old man were to tell Rudra to go and slit his own wrist, he would only ask one question: wrist of which hand. If the old man were to tell him to die, Rudra would only inquire, how, when and where. But what shocked him the most, was the

Pain of body, mind or heart, means the land is fertile for God to begin cultivating on your soul, my son. But if you let pain make you bitter, negative, mean, vindictive.... Ah son, you have lost the greatest opportunity to walk in the shadow of God. But if you allow pain to harvest the good in you my child, then the kingdom of heaven is yours; not only when you exhale your last and leave your physical frame, but even when you live and with every breath you take while you live. The cross will remain, but your shoulders will get more strength. The whip will lash on your body but the balm of God will not allow pain to touch you. The kingdom of heaven is filled with wonders son; the greatest wonder of all, is to convert pain to God consciousness...

realization, that if the old man were to even command him to go on living and living with grace, he would only nod and get his act together. Rudra was certain, as convinced as he was of his own existence and his love for his children, that he would not only die but also keep living for this old man. Why? He didn't know and didn't care.

Then something strange happened. The old man raised his hand and caressed Rudra's face. Rudra could feel the hot blood from the old man's bleeding palm wet his right cheek. What followed further shocked him. He began to cry. Tears rolled down his cheeks, mixed with the blood on his face and streamed down his throat. At first the tears rolled down gently but moments later Rudra put his head on the old man's chest and sobbed like a child.

ALL THE WHILE Rudra wept, the old man gently caressed his back. Rudra felt a strange sense of energy move up and down his spine. He felt his breathing settle and slowly he lifted his head and knelt by the old man. Rudra was certain that whatever was happening was out of the realms of normalcy. Nothing was normal anymore. Not the old man; oh no, nothing was normal about the old man. He was badly injured but he still kept smiling like some thinner version of the laughing Buddha. He was injured but not once had he winced in pain or moaned in agony. Then there were his divine eyes. They were so restful, non judgmental and full of compassion that one could keep looking into them, feel safe and most importantly, feel forgiven. It was as if they conveyed to one and all, that, all was well and the God of all beings was far more graceful and cool than what the priests and interpreters of Holy Books made Him out to be.

That every saint had a past and every sinner a future and that the God who made the Grand Canyon and the Himalayas with the majestic Mt. Everest was also the same God who took the time off to paint a different sunrise and sunset each day and who made sure that the trees that lay unattended on the roadside and by the parking lot, were equally nourished with morning dew; that it was time a particular caterpillar living a wayward life somewhere in Africa was transformed into a butterfly; and that when a baby cried, the mother could automatically interpret the reason for the wail of her baby, that the little one had opened its small mouth wide open and screamed its little guts, out of hunger-wet nappy-colic pain-sleep-boredom or it just was in need of a warm tender hug.

The old man was as normal as the advent of spring on Mars or mankind all of a sudden realizing that it was best for its own sake to live in peace and share resources amongst the starving and the dying and with those in desperate need.

"This Fakir thinks you don't have much time to live son?"

Rudra should have been shocked for a number of reasons. First of all, the old man spoke English. He looked like a Moslem-sage and usually these sages conversed only in the native language of the land. Secondly, and most importantly, the old man's prediction was dead on right. Rudra did have a very short time on planet earth. Mercifully it would be spent in peace. Lastly, not only was all this 'spoken' to him in sign language and lip-mouthing but surprisingly, Rudra understood everything. That he could understand sign language or grasp lip reading so easily no longer shocked him. The only thing that surprised him was the casual manner in which he himself accepted all these abnormalities. Normalcy was just a state of mind; just a conditioning. Who is to decide what is normal and what is not? Rudra was way past knowing or caring.

THE OLD MAN allowed Rudra to attend to his wounds. He had suffered a severe gash on the scalp but fortunately only minor cuts and bruises on the elbows. Obviously, the old man had landed on his back, with the elbows and then the scalp taking the brunt of the fall. Rudra without a word cleansed the wounds with antiseptic and then bandaged the head and the right elbow with the amazing deftness and grace of a drunk-blind bull running at full gallop in a china shop; but he did all this with infinite tenderness.

"I know my nursing skills are horrible but that is the best I can do. We will get a professional doctor to do a better job." Rudra spoke slowly. He was not certain whether the old man could hear. Why else would he speak to him in sign language and only mouth the words and not speak them out. The old man smiled and patted Rudra's face.

"Don't worry. There is nothing to be ashamed of, if you have given your best to whatever you are doing, son. Only mankind is interested in results. Nature only wants to know your intentions. A dog just wags its tail happily. It is not bothered about whether its tail has wagged with finesses or whether it looks funny. It only knows how to love its master. It gives its best. It may make a mess of things regularly but then you don't mind. Why? Because you know the dog's heart is in the right place. It is giving its best to you. The same way Nature and God don't judge you by your performance or your results. They just want to know whether your intentions are proper, your heart is in the right place and that you are giving your best to whatever you are doing. Every thing else is just pure statistics."

Rudra was still amazed at their form of communication. Though the old man had not spoken a word aloud, Rudra understood him perfectly.

Rudra remembered his grandmother, who used to tell him often, that it was 'why you did-what you did', that was more important than, 'what came about what you did' that really mattered to the heaven's above. That the Angels heard the purity in the prayer rather than the prayer itself or the fancy words mouthed; and that work done intelligently was far superior to tremendous hard work done without much thought but the intention of the labour was way far above intelligence, effort or results.

Success is a very complex term. What could be success for one, could mean failure for another. Take creation itself. For so many it is a roaring success. And for so many, it is an unmitigated failure.

Only mankind is interested in results. Nature only wants to know your intentions.

RUDRA PARKED HIS van under a benevolent banyan tree, which gave ample shade to them. Also the lovely fragrance and the backdrop music of a hundred odd birds perched on the various branches of the tree made the setting more pleasant than it really was. In reality, they were in the middle of nowhere, with barren land all around, and vehicles passing, miraculously without colliding with each other. Travelling in India, on a national highway, is not for the faint-hearted. Each vehicle moves with the single-minded purpose to reach its destination by defying physics and the law of velocity and gravity. To travel fast and reach one's destination, either speed or sheer bulk or exasperating maneuvering is used and if you are really unlucky, you could have a vehicle move towards you at frightening knots an hour, with all the combinations put together.

"They go through life just like that. In a great hurry but if you ask them why, they don't have an answer. Maybe they might reach an hour or two earlier, but most often, those hours don't make a difference. All in a hurry to reach a destination they are anyway going to reach. During the entire journey, the driver is tense, making rash moves, miraculously avoiding oncoming traffic, abusing other drivers and worrying all those in the vehicle. Nobody really enjoys the ride. The sensible go off to sleep. The wise leave it to their Master. The anxious make a nuisance of themselves and the driver drives on wanting to overtake, speed up and be able to do better timing than his boss or his neighbour or the driver ahead of him. They forget that life is not a hundred metre dash but a long marathon. I am hungry. Do you have anything in that black haversack apart from whisky and gin bottles?"

Rudra smiled sheepishly. It was a closed haversack bag and the old man knew of the contents without opening it. He thought hard. Did he have anything to eat? Yeah.

The old man's eyes lit up and he gleefully took the packet that Rudra handed to him. The old man said a short prayer and insisted that Rudra share the comestible.

Then, Rudra watched this sage who could read his future, know the contents of a zipped up haversack and philosophize on life and the very heavens itself, for the next few minutes enjoy like a child, the wonders of a Kit-Kat chocolate bar.

THE SUN WAS about to set but the two men were in no hurry to move on. It was decided that Rudra would call the old man Baba.

Now the word Baba has different meanings. On face value, Baba means 'father'. Especially in villages in Maharashtra, children address their father as Baba. The word could also mean, 'old man', but spoken with respect. It does not sound disparaging when spoken in Hindi. When you call somebody 'an old man' in English, it sounds as though you are mocking him or being rude. But when you say Baba in India, it means

' I respect your age and the experience you have earned through living'. Surprisingly, this very word is also used to call out to a child. Like when you say to a kid, 'Baba, I know this medicine tastes like horse shit but please swallow it'. Or, it can also be said in a frustrated manner, like, ' ok Baba, you want to marry that man who should have been strangulated at birth either by his mother or the family doctor, then go ahead, but don't tell me I did not email you and warn you so'.

But the best association of the word is when it is used in its spiritual context. Baba means Master, Guru, Lord of one's destiny. Thus, in India, you have Masters known by this word. It means Father-Guru-Everything. Thus Sai Baba of Shirdi, Meher Baba, Baba Nanak, Kamu Baba, Makhdum Baba, Baba Nityanand and Muktanand and many Perfect Masters have the title Baba attached to Their names. You really are blessed if you can die with 'Baba' on your lips.

Thus Baba it was.

"WHY DON'T WE spend the night here?" Baba gesticulated. Sometimes he 'spoke' and Rudra lip-read. Often Baba gestured with his hands and 'spoke' together. Whatever mode of communication was adopted, Rudra somehow understood him effortlessly. It was bizarre. It was even eerie, this strange grasp of the unspoken. This silent interaction, whether through signs or lip reading, made Rudra feel very close to the old man; closer than he had felt with anybody else, ever.

Of course, one thing became clear to Rudra. Baba could hear very well. He was far from deaf. Sometimes, Rudra felt the old man could even hear what was not spoken.

For some reason, Baba did not speak aloud. Maybe

he did not want to speak aloud. Just as, a large majority of folks, who had no hearing impairment but still refused to hear. Or worse, make believe they could not hear, only because, in reality, they did not want to listen.

One needs to be open to communication. Open to the fact that there are different manners of dialogue; various modes of exchange of ideas and innumerable ways of listening; and very often words could be voiced and heard in so many different ways.

The One who makes the thunder roar, also hears a butterfly sigh.

So THEY SPENT the night under the banyan tree. Rudra had a few tins of soup, cans of beans and chicken, and he never travelled without his stove and basic essentials. He very often spent days in his van, camping on mountain tops or on the outskirts of towns and villages, whenever he wanted to spend time alone but not be holed up in a stuffy room.

There were days and nights when he withdrew so within himself that it made no sense to be amongst the living; mankind, other animals, whatever. He was not aware what name to give that phase; what tag to label

The same way Nature and God don't judge you by your performance or your results. They just want to know whether your intentions are proper, your heart is in the right place and that you are giving your best to whatever you are doing. Every thing else is just pure statistics."

that silence; whether it was negative and destructive or just diving deep within and exploring the unknown without really grasping anything on the conscious plane. Earlier, he would define these phases as depressions but he wasn't too certain anymore.

He had battled often with depression and very often nearly succumbed to the enchanting call of death; the blissful tune that he could hear, that conveyed eternal silence, perpetual slumber. He really did want to end his life and sleep and never ever wake up; not on planet earth or the beyond. Not even to hear the harp (he never really fancied the instrument) or ogle at the celestial beauties that frequent heaven (the concept of heaven rammed down the mystified throats of young Indians). No. He just wanted to die and never wake up to any sort of consciousness: physical, emotional, mental or astral. He wanted to become nonexistent.

The pain was unbearable. His heart often felt it would tear open, with the constant throb of anguish and the unceasing lashing of grief. Tears that welled but never were allowed to flow through the eyes. He did cry but that was really rare and never encouraged. Tears, just like howling wind, gushing from some deep void in the cosmos, would just gush down, leaving him wrecked and wretched. They came announced: when watching a movie; reading a book; hearing a song; seeing a child embrace a loved one; chuckling of kids; a kid all alone with sadness writ in its eyes; two kids on a motor bike with their parents or their dad; cartoon network; McDonalds with kids enjoying themselves with their parents... too many reasons or may be no reason what so ever. He tried to never let himself lose control but without a warning memories of the past would catch up with him and rip his heart and trample his soul.

Nothing made sense anymore. His canvass of life was devoid of colour. His palate had lost all sense of taste. He felt like a corpse but of course, he still existed and he saw his life as an oxymoron. A living corpse belongs to neither world. Planet earth so often has no use for the living, thus a living corpse is redundant and the spirit world obviously has no use of somebody with a gross body. 'Only Members who possess a *spirit* permit can enter. Ha! Ha!'

At times like that, he would get into his faithful black van and like a good corpse withdraw from the world. But as hunger and thirst (just like other messy functions of the body, which are not really concerned or impressed whether the heart and the mind are getting the shit kicked out of them), demand attention, Rudra always had a well-stocked van of liquor, water, books, films, food tins and gasoline.

"Never, ever, eat alone," gesticulated the old man. Rudra nodded. He had heard and read often that one did not need words to communicate, well, now he understood and agreed. "You might say that you spend all your time alone but you know boy, only a fool thinks he is ever alone. God and your Guides, your Spirit Guides are always there around you. It is so selfish and ungrateful to eat without offering all you eat and drink to Them and inviting Them to share whatever you eat along with you.

The One who makes the thunder roar, also hears a butterfly sigh.

"Just imagine your Master and your Guides, all sitting next to you, and you, gorging yourself with all the nonsense most people eat, without even inviting Them to join in. Just because you can't see Them does not mean They are not around you. Wouldn't you say that was selfish and sad? Remember never ever think you are alone. And if you really think you are alone; if you really are under the illusion that it is you and you alone that gets things done, then slowly your Guides leave, as there are innumerable souls who need help and guidance and believe they can be helped from the other side. So the Guides try and try to communicate with you and make their presence felt and then sigh and move on and then you really are alone. If you have any sense you realize you are an extraordinary ass and call out to Them to rejoin you. You call out once and They are back with you... of course, only when They feel you really want Them to be with you. They are sensitive. Sometimes a shade too oversensitive; it takes all to make even the spirit world." Baba smiled and Rudra realized it was the most beautiful smile in all of creation.

"You really think Masters and Guides are around all of us?"

"Guides are there around all. Of course Masters and Guides depend upon the spiritual and karmic grade of each individual. Those who are very old souls or high souls, obviously have more evolved spirits guiding them and always around them. A child going to the first grade has a teacher who is suitable for the child and a grown up doing his or her Master degrees or a Doctorate in philosophy has a different kind of tutor. Please, I am not comparing the teachers; only their specialized skills.

It also depends upon what the individual soul needs to learn and experience. Thus, there are a lot of prerequisites that determine the Guides and light workers. Your grades determine your Guides and Masters. Of course, if for lifetimes you have worshipped and served a Master, obviously that Master will be around you all the time in every life time; physically or spiritually. Guiding you to move upward spiritually and enhance your karma. You might not even realize that your Master and your Guides are guiding and helping you. You might not even be worshiping your Master. You might have not even heard about Him or Her or seen your Master in this lifetime, but your Master is there for you always. Just like a mother who feeds and tends to her child, irrespective whether the child is in the womb or a day old or well into its sixtieth birthday or retarded or blind or deaf or dumb... it doesn't matter. A million times more intense is the love of the Master towards all those who are in His or Her protection and clan. That is why we say that the Master or Guru is Brahman (Creator), Vishnu (Preserver) and Siva (Destroyer) and in fact the Master or Guru is God itself, all along working unceasingly to make certain that the disciple and devotee grows spiritually and becomes one with God. That is the aim of the Master; to make the devotee or disciple become one with God. Now if you don't mind, can I get something to eat before I faint with hunger and exhaustion as well as that noise that beetle is making? Do you know that God has made more than a few thousand varieties of bugs? Why? I don't know. Maybe He had just too much time on hand. Ha! Ha!"

As USUAL THE dreams made him toss and turn. He missed his kids. Yearned for them so much that he had no taste on his tongue, no colour in his vision, no music and rhythm in his life. He missed them so much that even death would not negate the ache; for the pain was no longer in his heart but had seeped its way into his soul.

He realized this while visiting the US. He had the good fortune of frequenting the most talked about streets and avenues on earth. Living the American dream. Visiting cities that millions of folks all over the world would give an arm and a leg, more perhaps, to frequent and absorb.

He viewed the most fantastic sunsets and was surrounded by surreal natural beauty; something that always held his fascination. He had both, the best of the material and the spiritual world.

And it made no difference to him.

He might as well have been in his van, or in a rented flat or lying down, eyes shut, fighting the demons at night. He respected American people (those born there as well as those who had made it their home) and their zest for life. But for him, being there made no difference. New York, California, Pennsylvania, New Jersey and their various glittering vibrant cities and lovely natural surroundings touched neither his heart nor his soul. And he was certain that even heaven would leave him with a similar sense of numbness.

Was that numbness *hell*? The type of hell that Holy Books keep talking on and on about. The raging fires of restless, negativity, guilt, jealousy, anger and the freezing depths of constant heartache, inertia, nightmares and the persistent need to sleep for ever.

How come nobody mentions this freaking side of hell? Why keep harping about having to die, to be thrown into those mythical raging fires and all the melodramatic stuff that goes to describing hell, which I presume is meant to scare us living mortals shitless? Why die when hell needed no visa or a dramatic shift of residence. Hell was here and now. Hell is nothing but a state of mind.

He woke up and as usual, for a few seconds, took time to decipher his place of dwelling. He remembered incidents of the previous day and his eyes searched for the old man. Not seeing him on the makeshift bed, Rudra got out of his sleeping bag and looked out of the van. He could see the farms and a few sheep grazing but the old man was not in sight. Rudra was aware that the old man was close by, for he could smell the fragrance of the tobacco, which the old man smoked in his *chillum*, a local pipe, very popular amongst the hippie folks and sages in India.

Never give anybody the power to hurt you son. Never give anybody the power to affect your peace of mind. That is asking for hell my boy. That power should be given only to your God and Master; never to any human being or any other living creature. Mankind was made too much in a hurry to be trusted with something as precious as one's peace of mind. Love everybody but trust only God and your Master. Nobody else.

Rudra sat up, bowed to the rising sun, and then got out of the van. He had slept on the floor of the van, while the old man had slept on the makeshift bed. Seeing Rudra, the old man smiled.

"You are a very troubled sleeper. You toss and turn and moan and groan and it is strange that for a man who looks so serene and calm, you carry a very heavy cross. Not good, young man. Carrying a cross has done nobody any good. Even My Brother was crucified so savagely but then He was something else." It was obvious the old man spoke of Jesus Christ. It was not what he spoke but the way his eyes became tender and his face softer, that gave Rudra gooseflesh all over his body. It was as though the old man knew the Son of God personally and longed to meet up with Him again. As though both of them knew each other only too well and each felt incomplete without the other.

"How are you feeling, Baba?"

"Better than a mule but not as good as a horse. Ha! Ha." Rudra smiled and entered the van to make tea. "Once I have your ginger and mint tea I will be better than a horse too." Rudra felt a tingle go up his spine. He got out of the van and faced the old man.

"How did you know that I make ginger and mint tea?"

"My son, just keep your eyes open. You will learn more about an individual that way than by reading his astrological chart. I saw your ginger and mint packet next to your tea and sugar bottle. Its just power of deduction son. It is as obvious as the fact that you miss your kids. You have gone through hell. You are a good man who has messed up because you did not want to take certain decisions that you thought would hurt those near you but then they have used that compassion of yours and finished you with their hate and their venom and their ridiculous allegations.

"I can read it in your eyes. See it in your face. You know son, giving a person the benefit of doubt a few times is very noble. After that it is being stupid. And still after that it is being masochistic and asking for certified hell. Never give anybody the power to hurt you son. Never give anybody the power to affect your peace of mind. That is asking for hell my boy. That power should be given only to your God and Master; never to any human being or any other living creature. Mankind was made too much in a hurry to be trusted with something as precious as one's peace of mind. Love everybody but trust only God and your Master. Nobody else. Don't doubt but then don't get surprised too. There is only one being who can never let you down. That is your God and Master. "

"Sometimes I think God and Master can hurt you the most. Especially if you have placed all your faith in Them and They betray your trust. Shatter your faith…"

"Faith my son is a very loaded word. We believe that true faith encompasses all of creation and beyond. True faith is far deeper and nobler and closer to God and Master, than all the philosophies and the Great Books put together. In fact, put all that which is spiritual on one scale and put true faith on the other and I still feel the other side will not weigh as much as the scale on which true faith reposes. But son, there is a great difference in what I call true faith and what you refer to as faith." The old man lit his *chillum* again and took a few deep puffs. He then smiled and passed the *chillum* to Rudra. He took it and inhaled deep. Felt the warm smoke travel into his body and felt the sweet taste of tobacco tingle his tongue. "Get the tea and then I'll tell you the difference between the two types of faith. One is like a real diamond. The other, equally beautiful, is made of glass. Diamonds don't break; glass inevitably shatters."

WHILE PREPARING TEA, Rudra all of a sudden remembered his trips abroad. USA, Singapore, Sri Lanka, Dubai. For no real reason he remembered spending hours at the Heathrow Terminal (Terminal Three). Remembered the day distinctly. Sitting at the Starbucks Coffee café, watching the world go by. People of various nationalities, colours and races, moved around him, all occupied with their own world! Each person moved about in his or her own world. How many worlds must there be? People carrying varied baggage, some seen, most unseen; the latter being carried for years and lifetimes, in their heart-mind-soul. He remembered being served so tenderly by a man of colour, little darker than him, but his smile and genuine warmth so much deeper than what Rudra would ever bring himself to nurture.

Hours earlier, he had been with Viya, who was more close to him than his brother. Days spent with him and his darling of a pet, Spens.

Viya, who, those days, was going through the leanest of phases; emotionally and financially, but who refused to be beaten by destiny. He kept getting up and looking life in the eye and more importantly, with a calm heart and a broad smile. He understood what Rudra was going through. They had spent those days, two men, thrashed by life and fate, bumming around. Walking the streets of Manhattan. Late nights at the Village, perched on wooden chairs, outside cafés, having Bud Light or coffee. Taking the last train back home to New Jersey and then sleeping when the night reluctantly let the dawn make her presence felt.

Two men, who refused to get bitter or negative. Yes, they hurt. That was only natural but they refused to let the smile or the glow vanish from their eyes and heart. They discussed their lives and their past and knew that they would not open their hearts or their wounds or nightmares to anybody else. Only to those closest and they didn't have many close to them anyway.

Of course, even Viya, was aware that Rudra was going downhill. He too feared that Rudra might one day end his life. All alone, without leaving a message or a goodbye note. What was there to write about? Fate, destiny, karma, whatever, had already torn most of the pages worth reading.

No good deed ever goes unnoticed and no wrong thought or action goes unseen and unaccounted. The balance sheet is in your very soul. All accounts are kept in one's own soul, updating automatically everything like a computer so advanced that mankind will take eternity and longer to even come remotely close to it. Nature is a phenomenal accountant and the soul is the keeper of the accounts. You don't have anybody else keeping a tab on your actions. Your very soul keeps all the accounts and then decides what is the best course to remedy or reward itself.

"Does a man have to do severe penance to get a hot cup of tea?" Baba spoke but with a broad smile.

"Lost in thoughts…"

"That is dangerous son. Thoughts are dangerous. Very. Come on out, we will have tea under the tree and smoke and smile and live and die a little and talk about real faith. Come on out son."

"You know there are various types of faith, son. Just as there are various dimensions to heaven and hell. For instance, take those who go to heaven…"

"Is there some place called heaven?"

"Let me rephrase your question and throw it back at you. First of all, do you believe there is a Power that has created, nurtured and can destroy all of creation? In simple English, do you believe in God?"

Rudra nodded an affirmative. He could deny his very existence but he knew there was a God. Even though that God seemed to be on an over-extended vacation in some remote part of the galaxy where reception was rather poor and communication took place only in spurts and was most often, unintelligible and non-comprehensible. But he did firmly believe that there is a Power who has gone through considerable pain and effort to create the universe, galaxies, planets, stars, dinosaurs, humans, ants, amoeba, art, yeah yeah, even women and hundred of thousand species and sub species, whatever, that meant. Yeah, he believed in the Old Man.

"So, you do believe in God and if you do believe in God, then you must also believe that our God is not partial, unjust, demented or senile? Good! You believe in a sane God. Thank God for that. That means you also believe in reincarnation…"

"Just because I believe in a hazy way that there is a God somewhere around doesn't mean that I believe in all the metaphysical jazz dished out for the last few thousand years..."

"But if you believe in God then you must believe in reincarnation?"

"Why Baba?"

"My dear goat, if there is a God then that God is just. If that God is just then He will not act on a whim or a fancy or be partial. If He is just then He will treat all in the same fair and unbiased manner. But if you don't believe in reincarnation, then you believe in an unjust God or else there can be no logic or explanation, that some children are born on the street dying for food and water and fighting for survival, while some children have all the comforts and luxuries that can be thought of by their parents and the marketing world. If you don't believe in reincarnation, then why are some born blind, lame, dumb and deaf, retarded, crippled in more ways than possible while some have such good health that it is virtually nauseous? By the way, that does not mean I am implying that those who are born retarded or crippled are paying for their sins. Not in a million years. I will explain that later. I am not referring to an angry GOD here. In fact, most often, God leaves the entire planning to you. Anyway we will discuss that, too, later. Now back to the former subject of why do some go through life all alone, miserable, poor, bullied, tortured, abused, discarded and some go through life as though it is nothing but an extension of heaven? Why, my confused lamb, do some moan and groan all night while some sleep the sleep of the angels? In short, my son, why is there such disparity? So either you believe there is no God and thus no law and no justice and thus all the imbalance makes perfect sense or there is a God and as HE cannot be unjust, then there is some sense in the madness and reincarnation becomes the only logical conclusion."

"Why?"

"Ok, let's reason more. Give me more of that of thing you insist on calling tea. Ha ! Ha! Reincarnation is nature's way of settling all pending issues and allowing us to go through all experiences necessary to take us up the ladder of evolution. Without reincarnation we would not have the opportunity to work out our destiny and work at our karma. Tell me noble Rudra, one who tosses and turns and moans all night long and then makes tea that would make Satan proud, why do some people have to go through very difficult experiences all through their lives while some go through life as though walking in the park?

Why are some born so rich that they have lost count of their wealth, while millions have to count every single paisa or cent or penny just to keep body and soul together? Some are born healthy while some have ill health stalking them through their lives. Some are so very fortunate that though they have no talent or craft or intelligence they still have all the luck and fame and wealth while so many have all the talent and genius but have to go through life unappreciated and unrecognized and miserable for they know they are far above the normal but still have to follow the path of mediocrity. Some are born lepers while some have the physical beauty of the Gods. Why? Not because God prefers some and abhors others? That is not in God's DNA. God has no favourites. God does not take sides.

"You have played lots of outdoor games, so I will give an example, in the context of games and playing. In football or a basketball, there are set rules. You play by those rules. If you don't play by those rules you are fouled or even removed or banned from playing future games or penalized. Why? Because you did not follow certain rules of the game, and my boy, life is the biggest of all games and has the most intricate rules. You play by the rules, great. You don't, you pay the consequences. Those consequences might even be passed on to the next game. So often a player is shown the red card and disqualified to play in the next game. Very recently your Indian captain was debarred from playing a few one day cricket matches as he was accused of wasting too much time setting the field and making the over rate way too slow. So he was banned from a few games. Which means for his mistake in one game, he had to pay a penalty in the next few games too. It means his penalty was passed on. Just imagine the player saying he doesn't remember anything about the penalty. That's fine, others are aware of the penalty, those who keep a

Every time you do something right, you help tilt the balance in favour of truth and that contribution affects the vibration within the cosmos. Each one of us sending out the right vibration can then help change the mindset of more and more people till the world throbs with positive vibrations and right actions. Each of us matters to providence and has a say in creation and evolution.

tab on such things. The player might cry foul and say that all are impartial but there are rules and whether he remembers the penalty or not, there are the rule makers who remember all and they can't change the rules as that would be unfair to all the other players. It would also set a wrong precedent. Of course, reincarnation is not about penalties and punishments. That is a small part of the whole magnificent web of creation.

"There are many who work so hard and use their time and intelligence and common sense in a manner that what others finish in three years or semesters, they finish off in one year or in one semester. So if it is a five-year course, the intelligent and hard worker might finish it off in three years. All the hard work will reap a good harvest. The person who has put in real hard work, studied day and night, used intelligence and has sacrificed pleasure and leisure and thus finished a five-year course in three years will have a head start in life by two years. Now imagine the other class mates screaming foul play and partiality and accusing the management of unjust conduct and insisting that either they too get the same two year privilege or the genius be forced back into the university and made to stay on for two years. Would that be fair? No! You reap what you sow. You earn what you deserve. We believe that no effort goes unnoticed or in vain. No study or craft or art or acquired skill goes to waste. It is carried forward to other life times. That is why some are so intuitive in certain things. Some are born intelligent or are geniuses in certain fields; arts, science, technology, cooking, gardening, driving, speaking or noble living. These souls have toiled and spent lifetimes working hard. Effort never goes waste. Nature and providence only see intention and effort. That is why we believe that one is never too young or old to learn something. You will reap the benefits of that knowledge; in this life or the next.

"Don't you think it is wrong to begrudge somebody or God for intelligence or genius? That person has earned it. Nature does not hand out free gifts to just a few. Either it's to all or nobody. It either gives to all or one has to earn it. That is why reincarnation becomes so important. No good deed ever goes unnoticed and no wrong thought or action goes unseen and unaccounted. The balance sheet is in your very soul. All accounts are kept in one's own soul, updating automatically everything like a computer so advanced that mankind will take eternity and longer to even come remotely close to it. Nature is a phenomenal accountant and the soul is the keeper of the accounts. You don't have anybody else keeping a tab on your actions. Your very soul keeps all the accounts and then decides what is the best course to remedy or reward itself. That is why reincarnation is so important. The soul hates to carry baggage. The soul decides to go through certain experiences to teach oneself all about the Ancient Plan. There is nobody waiting to toast your you-know-what in eternal fire! Heaven and hell are decided by one's own soul. We'll speak about this later now. All in good measure and time. Anyway let's smoke a pipe and have some more of that ghastly tea you make with so much love. I like it. Ha!"

THE STREAM WAS Baba's idea. He shut his eyes and

informed Rudra that apart from making ghastly tea (which the old man loved), there in the distance was a wooded area where a stream flowed. It was a pleasant day. Cloudy sky. A cool breeze caressed their faces and relaxed their bodies.

Rudra remembered his childhood. It was a perfect day to play with his neighbourhood friends. He thought of them and his heart cringed. So many dead and those living all scattered and battered by life. But today was really a perfect day to be outdoors. The banyan tree with innumerable birds perched on its hospitable branches felt like home. Rudra observed the tree. He felt bonded with it. Though they had shared barely a few hours together, not a word spoken between them, he felt strangely very close to it. There was a world revolving round the tree; birds perched on its branches; squirrels running up and down; butterflies circled the vines and ants moved in long lines along its thick branches doing whatever they were involved with. What amazed Rudra was that he had entered this world by sheer accident. Thousands of vehicles passed the tree daily without giving it a glance. Forget giving it a second glance. Even a glance was highly unlikely. But Rudra was certain that this tree too played an important role in creation. That this tree too had a say in global warming, the monsoon, nature's equilibrium, the

Whenever a child calls out to me with love, real love, I am there with that child. If the child wants me to be with him or her, forever, then the child needs to love me that way. All I need is love, selfless love. Be in the moment my son.

fragrance in the air, in pollination, in supporting innumerable activities important to nature and to the small world of birds, squirrels, ants, butterflies and all the other life that throbbed and revolved round and within this silent, humble, inconspicuous tree.

"The same way, my son, each individual matters to mother nature and to God," said Baba, looking deep into Rudra's eyes. "Every person is a world within himself or herself. Every soul makes a contribution and even has a small say in creation and the running of this universe and the innumerable galaxies that inhabit the universe. Just like this tree, we matter and contribute to the running of things on mother earth and also in the spirit world. Every time you do something right, you help tilt the balance in favour of truth and that contribution affects the vibration within the cosmos. Each one of us sending out the right vibration can then help change the mindset of more and more people till the world throbs with positive vibrations and right actions. Each of us matters to Providence and has a say in creation and evolution. And that way we have a say even in the spirit world. The vibrations you emit help even the spirit world. The spirit world we will talk about later. Now let us go and wash our selves in the cool spring and then eat something and then be on our way. You have a lot of work to do."

Rudra was no longer surprised about how Baba knew his innermost thoughts but wondered what work the old man had in store for him. Also he wanted to ask him two questions. The first one was on faith and the second one on why some were born with so many crippling defects. He had been told that it was God's way of punishing people. But Rudra was certain that his God was not a barbarian.

ACCORDING TO BABA, the stream was silently gushing in a small wooded area, a kilometre away from where the van was parked. At first Rudra was apprehensive of taxing Baba with the walk but five minutes later, he realized that the old man walked fast and without any sign of exertion.

It certainly was a good day for a walk. The clouds had moved in and blocked the sun, thus allowing the cool breeze to make the walk less of an exertion and more of a stroll. They walked in silence. The field was barren and Rudra realized that if only the powers-to-be concentrated on providing the right kind of infrastructure to the farmers nobody would die of hunger in his country. Providing water through irrigation and making certain that water resources were channeled in a manner that the farmer did not have to depend only on four erratic months of monsoon was the only rational solution. Yes, it would cost an astronomical sum but look at the obvious advantages. First of all, there would be employment for millions of people who would be needed to set up the national irrigation system. Once the farmer could till the land all year through, food would be available to all. Millions of farmers would be able to live a dignified life. They would no longer be forced to commit suicide just because the monsoon failed. They would be able to focus on educating their young and safeguarding their old. Also employment would be needed through the year for agriculture. If the farmer can procure water all year, through irrigation, then seventy per cent of the country's population would be able to work all year through. Their purchasing power would increase thus over-all demand would increase which in turn would complement industrial growth. Export of food grain would go through the roof. Migration to the cities would reduce. All this could become a reality if only agricultural activity were made possible throughout the year. Borrow money from world banks, get the big time multinationals to contribute, make certain the top thousand corporate houses chip in, spend less on bureaucratic nonsense...for God sake, if a country is primarily agricultural, then it should focus on agriculture; agriculture needs water all year through.

They entered the wooded area. It was a small forest but not dense and not vast; quarter of a mile in length and breath, at the most. The moment they entered it, the temperature further dropped and the light dimmed. It also took a while for Rudra to adjust to the different aromas that assailed him. It reminded him of Swami Rama's Himalayan Institute in Pennsylvania, in the US.

The stream of life flows through all of us. One needs to connect with it and enter it. It is sometimes lost in the woods of thoughts, confusion, greed and day-to-day life. It is there in all. Some lead their entire life never once appreciating its beauty or being cleansed by its cool waters. But those who find it within are refreshed and strengthened by it at all times, whenever they so desire. One needs to slow down, hear the flow within and merge with it. You people call it meditation. I call it going inward.

According to Rudra, it was for sure one of the most scenic places in the world. Forests, lake, streams, deer roaming around, spiritual seekers going about their work, the entire ashram surrounded by mountains and, as far as the eye could see, the sprawling sky. And in spite of all the natural beauty, Rudra had nearly killed himself in that very beautiful forest, with a lake, streams and deer roaming. Recalling those moments, even now made Rudra's blood freeze. It was as though something within him, much more powerful, nudged and pushed him and tried its level best to drown him in depression, where suicide and only suicide was the way out. And for some reason Rudra didn't want to kill himself, not because he didn't want to die but because he did not want to die the death of a coward and he remembered kneeling down in that forest and crying to Baba for help and then after a while he felt warmth and hope and energy fill him up; as though nature, in Her mercy opened her arms wide and embraced him and consoled him and eventually healed him; at least healed him enough to be able to continue living. That day, Rudra had glimpsed into the mind of millions of those who live on the periphery of sanity.

"I was with you then. I heard your cry. I held you in my arms. Whenever a child calls out to me with love, real love, I am there with that child. If the child wants me to be with him or her, forever, then the child needs to love me that way. All I need is love, selfless love. Be in the moment my son. Enjoy this forest and these surroundings and these moments so that the soul can then bathe in these memories."

Rudra nodded. He knew what the old man said was

the only way to go about life. Being in the moment was being in the present and that was virtually being in tune with the Creator who was Presence and Present personified. Being in the moment made certain that you were not tormented by the past or burdened by the future. It was the way to sanity and health and, most of all, peace.

They could hear the stream flowing. With each step the sound only beckoned more. After a while the gushing of water had its own melody. Rudra breathed in deep. Baba walked ahead, his lips moving and Rudra was certain, the old man chanted the name of God. All the while, the old man was silent his fingers would move about, his lips would chant something that Rudra couldn't understand. Obviously, Baba spoke something in a different language. The sound of the birds, sometimes soft and sometimes screeching mingled with the melody of the stream and merged with the gentle breeze, contrasted with the sound of dry leaves that crackled under their feet. Baba wore thin wooden sandals, while Rudra had his slip-on shoes.

They saw the stream and both of them smiled, like two children. Rudra realized that it had been ages since he had felt a thrill over anything. Now with this strange old man, in this quaint forest, and this small stream, in some remote part of the country, gave him some surge of life, which he had thought had dried up within him.

They sat on the rocks near the stream and for a long time marveled at the beauty of nature. He could see the sky in patches, through the thousands of leaves that shaded them. He could hear the birds, sense the squirrels run about, feel the breeze on his face, breathe in the fragrance of the leaves and flowers and the wet earth that the stream flowed through. After a while, both of them, barefooted, taking care that their clothes did not get wet, entered the shallow stream. The water was cool and not even a few inches deep. The running water raced between their toes and caressed their feet, ankles and shins. Rudra bent down, took some cool water in his hand and washed his face, hair and the nape of his neck. Both of them stood like this for a long time. Baba then turned his face towards Rudra and smiled.

"The stream of life flows through all of us. One needs to connect with it and enter it. It is sometimes lost in the woods of thoughts, confusion, greed and day-to-day life. It is there in all. Some spend their entire life never once appreciating its beauty or being cleansed by its cool waters. But those who find it within are refreshed and strengthened by it at all times, whenever they so desire. One needs to slow down, hear the flow within and merge with it. You people call it meditation. I call it going inward. Your stream of life is drying up, like this stream. That is why it is just a few inches. As you spend more time going inward, the water rises and it washes you completely of all the tiredness and the muck and the pain and the slush of life." Saying this, Baba held

What is yours nobody can take away from you! What is not, you can bend heaven and hell, you will never retain it for long. That is the law of the universe. God is Just and God is merciful and God has given each and every creation of His, His very breath. God loves all, but son, for sure; He isn't blind.

Rudra's hand. Then he bent down, touched the water, shut his eyes and whispered something to the water. Seconds later Rudra felt the water rise.

IT WAS FOUR days since that magical moment the water rose. Baba never once discussed it. He just shrugged his shoulders and made certain that the subject of 'the rising' was never mentioned.

Both the men travelled to a port where finding a place to rent was virtually impossible. But Baba directed Rudra to a place where not only was there a small house available but it was sea facing. The cost was high but not as steep as the other places in the vicinity. Their place was virtually on the beach with innumerable cottages close by. Rudra on his own would never have been comfortable being so close to people but with Baba near him, nothing mattered.

Living with Baba ensured that there were certain dos and don'ts. The main one being, Rudra would not talk to Baba when with people. So much so that Rudra would behave as though Baba wasn't around. Not even look in Baba's direction. Rudra made a feeble attempt at objecting but he knew he was fighting a losing battle. Rudra could feel Baba's power. Positive surrender was not an option, it was as natural as breathing.

The next rule that the old man insisted on was that Rudra would not introduce Baba to anybody. He wouldn't even talk about Baba's physical presence.

The third directive was that Rudra would eat one meal a day, in a restaurant that was frequented by other people, without Baba's company.

The last being, Rudra would do all the work in the cottage by himself. No help from outside.

"Are you ok with the conditions."

"You're the boss."

"Only He is the Boss." Baba pointed skyward. Rudra nodded. They then strolled by the sea. It was early in the morning and they walked close to the water. They let the cold water wet their bare legs. Except for a few birds and a stray dog, the beach was desolate. Rudra realized that fortunately for him, tourists and health enthusiasts did not frequently inhabit this particular part of the waterfront. Most of the nearby cottages were owned as vacation resorts by the rich and this was not the time of the year for families or children to frequent beaches. Also the fact that it was not too close to the main city acted as a deterrent to the weekend crowd.

"I know you have many questions. I will answer them when the time's right, for you and for me too. Timing is of the essence. Otherwise, it is like throwing pearls to animals. If that happens, then both, the one who throws pearls and the person to whom the pearls are thrown to, are not ready. Sit."

They walked towards dry sand, settled down on soft, cool, golden brown earth and for a while they stared at the vast sea in front of them. Rudra was used to the sudden phases of silence. For hours, Baba would spend time, withdrawn deep within his own self, his lips silently moving, in prayer. Strangely, Rudra felt much calmer during those periods. As though in some strange way, the silence in Baba permeated Rudra's very being and calmed his turbulent subconscious mind. Rudra was used to silence. Being in the present moment often allowed him to be silent for hours at a stretch. But being silent along with Baba took him to another level of peace. With Baba, Rudra felt calm and silent, not only in mind but also in his heart and in every fibre of his body. It was as though from swimming on the surface, Rudra had begun to dwell deep and swim with the exotic aquatic inhabitants, in the ocean of life itself.

Rudra looked towards the water that appeared like a palette brimming with various colours. In parts, dull brown; very blue in others and yet more shimmering silver.

All of a sudden, he remembered his children and wondered what they were doing at the moment. Did they miss him? Did they love him? Did they believe in all the allegations thrown at him? Did they feel his pain and comprehend his love? Did they realize that he preferred to be silent rather then indulge in mud slinging? Did they understand that his silence was not his weakness but his cross, as it was only through silence that he would not get down to the same base level of counter accusations and ridiculous allegations? Often, he had been told to fight back. But fight whom? The mother of his children! How does one fight the one who has given birth to one's own blood and breath? He had been abused, wronged, character castrated but he remained silent for, at least, that way he did not cause

Silence, not only in words but also in thought is important. There is no sense being silent on the outside but inside burning and mentally abusing the world in general. Silence means tranquility; verbally and from within.

more harm to his children. His God knew the truth and that was fine with him. Yes, he too was at fault. But the honest truth was that he was not the only one at fault. Yes, he was no saint but he was certainly far from the devil he was being made out to be. The fact was that he was only human. The fact was that he had given his compassion to the wrong people.

He missed his children but he had one consolation that nobody could take away from him. Up to the time he had been with them, he had been a great father. He had given them his very soul. He had gone through hell and back in order to give them peace and a healthy childhood. And he had succeeded. Whatever mess took place, at least he had never involved them, even if that meant losing them forever. When the allegations and accusations were fired, he did not want them to be confused and caught in the crossfire. So he did what he thought was best. He did not retaliate. Heaven knew that he hurt, but that was all right. If by hating him, the kids could live a better and a less confused life, then so be it. It was better for them to hate him than live with confusion, guilt and fear. So he had relinquished his rights over them. One thing he was certain about, and that was, he would never use his kids to fight his war. He would never fire a gun from their tiny shoulders. He'd rather be dead. Be alone all his life. Be miserable all his life. Rather him than them; his little lives.

"It's all a drama son. The important thing is to live it with class. Silence has its own way of clearing its path. It takes time, but always remember, never ever resort of back biting, character assassination, mud slinging, fabrication; never. Whether one is right or in the wrong,

never ever resort to abusing somebody. As soon as you do that, you are in the wrong. Show your class boy. What is yours nobody can take away from you! What is not, you can bend heaven and hell, you will never retain it for long. That is the law of the universe. God is Just and God is merciful and God has given each and every creation of His, His very breath. God loves all, but son, for sure, He isn't blind. There is a season and a reason for every moment He has created. Eventually, we all are a part of Him and thus, we all are a part of each other. When you accuse and abuse and fabricate, son, you are abusing, accusing and fabricating against Him, your very own and your very own self. Silence, not only in words but also in thought is important. There is no sense being silent on the outside but inside burning and mentally abusing the world in general. Silence means tranquility; verbally and from within. Yes, you may hurt and be in pain and that is natural. When somebody cuts your hand, blood is going to ooze out and you are going to be in pain, but as long as there is no hatred, all is well. Hatred is the heaviest Cross of all, my son. Even the heavens pity the person who carries the Cross of Hatred, as this cross gets heavier and heavier by the moment. Always be in peace and be in silence. Even if you can be in one such state, you can live through nobly."
Baba, smiled and tears flowed down Rudra's face. He had never hated anybody. In spite of all that occurred, not once had he hated any of those involved in destroying him. Hatred burnt one's very soul. It ate into the very fibre of life. Nobody was that important.

"Faith comes in various intensities, intentions and in a way it is karmic. You can be born with faith or have faith introduced to you or have faith rammed into you. Faith can be inborn or nurtured. It can be your last option to retain your sanity or your anchor to go through life. Very often, when a person's back is to the wall, he will clutch on to either faith or hate. Both these emotions have their intensities and outcomes. The problem disappears, and so does faith or hate. Sometimes, it doesn't matter whether the problem remains or is solved or only gets worse; faith or hate remain. It depends on the maturity of the soul and one's upbringing and priorities. Anyway, lets discuss faith.

"Many expect, that just because they have faith, their life should be like a bed of roses. They demand that because they have faith, they should have no problems in life whatsoever. They feel that as they pray and chant the name of God, this entitles them to a life of no strife, no problems, free from all issues that can ruffle their tranquil but shallow waters. In short, they want life all smooth, no downs, all rosy. God forbid something, even slightly, goes against their conception of a perfect life and they begin to question God, creation and all the heavens above. They are of the firm belief that because they have taken the time out from their busy schedule and have prayed or performed a noble deed or indulged in charity or whatever, the heavens above should be at their call and mercy and instant gratification is not only desired but bloody well expected. This type of faith breaks easily. Along with the faith breaking easily, so does the heart. They are like children, who expect the very heavens to dance to their tune. They are good souls but young souls. Or souls that refuse to understand that God is not complex but the rules of life are entwined with the past and what is best for them in the future. When a child suffering from chronic asthma cries for an ice cream and the mother refuses to indulge him, aware that the ice cream could create a major health situation for the child and even hospitalization, then the deprivation of the ice cream is best for the child. The child may think otherwise but the mother knows best. A simple example but I assume you have got the point. As I told you before, throwing pearls to an animal, is not only a waste of pearls but speaks poorly about the one throwing the pearls too.

"I can assure you, God above has never ever wasted a pearl." Saying this Baba smiled and once again for a while remained quiet, as though allowing Rudra to assimilate what had been said. The old man looked so much like Sai Baba of Shirdi, with the white robe, beard, white bandana on the head, soft smile, deep tender eyes, that often Rudra would get tears in his eyes and would want to hug the old man. He loved the old man. Loved his temperament and simplicity.

He had realized that Baba was not at all particular about food and comfort. Feed him anything, howsoever simple or tasteless, howsoever complex and delicious, it was all eaten with the same grace and pleasure. Baba loved tea. Though he would often joke about the tea

Hatred is the heaviest Cross of all, my son. Even the heavens pity the person who carries the Cross of Hatred, as this Cross gets heavier and heavier by the moment. Always be in peace and be in silence. Even if you can be in one such state, you can live through nobly."

Rudra made, Rudra realized that he asked for the tea often. His *chillum*, his tea and his oil lamp were the only things the old man showed any sort of emotion towards.

"Now comes the second category of faith seekers or faith holders. The second category are advanced souls but still caught up in the transaction of give and take, though, in a different manner. Remember, we are not judging people or their faith or purity. We do not judge. Only He does and He is merciful. We are only discussing various types of faith and my belief that the one who has the ultimate faith is never ever let down. The second type of faith is more intense. In this type of faith, the person believes that because he or she has faith in God or Master, miracles are not only possible, but also guaranteed. They do not get upset when tough times come. They do not get shattered when fatal illnesses enter their life or the life of near and dear ones. They do not get paranoid when financial bankruptcy knocks at their door. They are certain, as confident as the sun shall rise in the east and set in the west, that their God or Master will pull them through the crisis with everything intact. Their usual mantra is ' I have full faith in my Master that He /She will take care of this problem... I have full faith in my God that this incurable disease will be cured.... I have complete faith that my Master will resolve this financial crisis." They even go to the extent of saying, 'this is not my problem, this is my Master's problem and I know He /She will take of it'. Or ' I have full faith in my prayers and I will sail through these issues'. What the person is trying to tell the Master or God is that, ' because I have full faith in you, you better take care of my problems' or ' don't let my faith down'. It is like treating your Master /God /your Prayers like an astral waiter. It's like telling your Master that just because I have come to your restaurant, the food better be good and you better deliver. Like saying 'I have invested my time and love and energy by having faith in you, so you'd better not let me down'. They are sure that their faith in their Master will resolve all issues. But sometimes, they have to go through their share of hard experiences. It is meant to be. In fact, the hard experiences are initiated by the Master to help them speed up their spiritual journey; to evolve them higher; to jump- start their spiritual growth. Or it could be very karmic and the Master feels that it's best to go through the experience and finish with your karma that is binding you on the physical plane. It is a complex web and it is the Master who knows what's best for you. Now to tell your Master, ' I have faith that you will not let this happen to me' is like telling your surgeon, ' I have full faith that you will not cut me up and you will not operate'. Then why go to the surgeon? And if you have gone to the surgeon, let the poor chap do his job. Yes,

Now we come to the most sublime form of faith. It's called graceful surrender. How do I define this form of faith? It is as finely chiseled as a straw of grass and as strong as the roots of a banyan tree. It is because of this faith that even God hesitates before letting loose His wrath. The God lover or Godchild, who has this faith flowing through the soul, has no expectations and no demands. There is no devotee or disciple too. There is just pure grace and surrender.

the operation will be performed in a manner no other surgeon can perform, but the operation is a must. Telling the surgeon I have full faith you will not perform the operation is not being very wise. Yes, there are times the surgeon might advise a way out of the operation. Or perform it in a manner that the recovery is phenomenal.

Make certain you never have to suffer from that medical problem ever again in your life. Make sure that your recovery is painless and quick and that you feel no pain during and after the operation. All this can be taken care of, but the operation is a must.

"Remember child, I am not judging these people, just explaining to you the different types of faith. Now, if the miracle does take place, the usual comment is, ' I knew my Master would never let me down'.

"My question is simple; is your faith conditional? Is your faith about yourself? If the catastrophe did take place, would it mean, your Master or God or Prayers have let you down? Would it mean, the Masters don't have it in Them as spiritual powerhouses to take care of your problem and that is why you went through the crisis? Does it mean, your Master or God has to keep proving His/Her power to you? In such cases, once again there are innumerable chances of faith breaking your heart, because once again your faith is conditional.

When you have a mantra that goes like ' I have faith in You that You will not let me down and only do all that I desire', then my son, that is very conditional faith. But remember, in this category, at least these children of God, are stronger and far more attuned with their Master, than most people. Spiritually too, they are more connected and really trying to be in constant touch with their Master and God. Thus prayers and spirituality come more naturally to them and day-to-day small issues are taken as minor tests from their Master, to be overcome with grace. It's only when the volcano erupts that their faith becomes conditional. But through the turmoil too, they are composed, confident and handle the situation with grace... but it is conditional... underwritten conditions apply... I have faith that my Master will deliver and not let me down."

Rudra knew both these types of faith clearly. He had oscillated all his life between these two types of faith. He had known people, good people, to belong to both these categories of faith. Sometimes their faith amazed you and sometimes made you wonder as to where the strength had fled. Mankind is a curious amalgam of heaven and hell; a strange contradiction of madness and genius, all rolled into one.

"Now we come to the most sublime form of faith. It's called graceful surrender. How do I define this form of faith? It is as finely chiseled as a straw of grass and as strong as the roots of a banyan tree. It is because of this faith that even God hesitates before letting loose His wrath. The God lover or Godchild, who has this faith flowing through the soul, has no expectations and no demands. There is no devotee or disciple too. There is just pure grace and surrender. If a disaster takes place, the child's very foundations are not shaken. The child also does not believe that ' I have full faith that my Master will resolve this problem' or ' my Master will never let me down' or ' I have complete faith in my Master/God/Prayer that this catastrophe/problem/

adverse situation will be taken care of and I will come out unscathed'. No.

"When a catastrophe does strike, the child of true faith, first of all is aware that whatever is taking place, is doing so, with the approval of his/her Master. Thus whatever unpleasantness is happening around, the child is certain that the hard experience has arrived only after his/her Master's approval. The person of true faith is certain that the Master has allowed the circumstances to enter his/her life for a purpose and the child does not want to know the reason or purpose. He or she is content in the knowledge that nothing, good or bad, pleasant or unpleasant, joy or grief, can enter his or her life, without the consent of the Master. If it has the consent of the Master, then whatever the unpleasant experience be... death, illness, separation, betrayal, bankruptcy, agony, grief, ill repute-allegations... whatever; it has arrived with a reason and the Master knows the reason and the Master has willed it and if something has been approved and blessed by the Master, then, that is all that matters.

"For, in this form of faith, the person's philosophy is simple: 'not a leaf moves and not a breath is taken without the approval of the Master'. Thus neither good experiences nor hard circumstances can enter the person's life without the Master's consent. Now this philosophy is not as simple as it sounds. Also, this is not a fatalistic approach to life. The person who lives this philosophy has left every breath, thought, action, repercussion, karma, life here and beyond in the care of the Master. The person gives his or her best to life and to every moment lived but leaves the consequences to

God/Master, without any expectation of reward or security or solace. In fact, in this form of faith, the person does not even expect protection from the Master, because to expect even protection of any sort, means harbouring some kind of expectation from the Master. In this form of faith, the child has left it all to the Master. The child is certain that whatever happens to him or her, it is happening with the will of the Master and whatever happens with the will of the Master is perfect and for the highest good.

"This form of faith requires total surrender. It is the most difficult but also the most sublime. It frees you from all expectations and also the agony of reward and punishment; success and failure; happiness and grief. You give your best to life and leave the rest to your Master. The Master knows best and that's that. So the philosophy is not, 'I have faith my Master will take care of me and will not let me down' but 'I have full faith in my Master and whatever happens my Master knows best and it is happening with my Master's permission and approval and as it is happening with my Master's

He or she is content in the knowledge that nothing, good or bad, pleasant or unpleasant, joy or grief, can enter his or her life, without the consent of the Master. If it has the consent of the Master, then whatever the unpleasant experience be... death, illness, separation, betrayal, bankruptcy, agony, grief, ill-repute, allegations... whatever; it has come with a reason and the Master knows the reason and the Master has willed it and if something has been approved and blessed by the Master, then, that is all that matters.

blessings, then nothing could be better for me than this'. The most important thing is that whatever takes place, is accepted gracefully and with positive surrender as the will of the Master. The consequences are accepted calmly and gracefully.

"Remember, it is easier said than done. This complete faith means annihilation of one's own self and identity. The person or this child of God becomes more like a dervish, a medium, an instrument of his/her Master. As the dervish fine-tunes his or her faith more and more and aligns his or her frequency or vibration with that of the Master, the child begins to lose his or her identity and takes on the identity of the Master. The more you lose yourself, the more you connect with your Master. The more you shed away yourself, the more space your Master gets to occupy. The less of you means more of your Master within you. Those who are really fine-tuned with their Master's frequency may, in the end, lose themselves completely and it is in them, their Master or their God resides. Then they become the true vessels or instruments where whatever they say, think, do, see, hear, all is through their Master, in fact it is done by their Master. Like mixing honey in cold milk. In the end, the honey and milk lose their individuality and merge with each other and the result is pure nectar.

"But remember there is a big difference between these dervishes, these children of true faith and those who are just fatalistic. First of all, a person of true faith gives his or her best to life, to the moment, to his or her Master. This is done without expectations of any sort. After that, whatever happens in his or her life, the person accepts it with grace and positive surrender. The dervish is not disgruntled or does not become negative or does not lose faith. In fact, he or she goes about life with the same intensity and love for the Master, more in fact, never less. But a fatalistic person's approach is remarkably different. This person uses the crutch of fate or destiny and not faith and surrender. A fatalist blames everything on destiny and God. Even the effort is never optimum, as the main philosophy of life is that effort and intention are overshadowed by stars and destiny and if all is destined, why overstretch for anything. If things don't go their way, the attitude is always ' what to do it wasn't in my stars' or ' God didn't want it so to hell with it'.

"Remember, both these type of people leave it all to God but notice the difference. The dervish gives his or her best without the thought of reward and consequence and leaves the result gracefully to the Master and accepts with positive surrender all that life bestows as the will of the Master. The fatalist never gives his or her best to life as the person believes that anyway all is destined by a God who is only interested in the balance sheet of

...the philosophy is not, 'I have faith my Master will take care of me and will not let me down' but 'I have full faith in my Master and whatever happens my Master knows best and it is happening with my Master's permission and approval and as it is happening with my Master's blessings, then nothing could be better for me than this'. The most important thing is that whatever takes place, is accepted gracefully and with positive surrender as the will of the Master. The consequences are accepted calmly and gracefully.

karma, so do whatever you like but in the end, whatever has to happen will happen. This person does not accept things with positive surrender but more with resignation and helplessness; even negativity, frustration and defeat. Thus there is a difference of heaven and earth between positive surrender and a fatalistic approach to life."

"You mean the person with true faith, this dervish or instrument of the Master, never gets agitated or upset or hurt with life and the outcome?"

"There are reactions; maybe temperamental outbursts. Like if somebody cuts you with a knife, you might react with a yell or a scream or even with a swearword. That's human. The important thing is after the initial reaction do you harbour ill-will, hate, anger in your mind and heart? Do you contemplate revenge? Do you accuse God and Master? Do you blame your Master for forsaking you? Do you keep asking 'why me'? These are character traits and what remains in your heart-mind-soul then determines your faith and your spiritual growth. For instance, a person might not react at all outwardly but hold anger and thoughts of revenge and retribution and also blame his or her Master for not being there when needed most. Now compared to that, a person might yell out for a moment and then compose himself and forgive and be in total acceptance of the situation and accept all that has taken place with positive surrender. Remember, reaction is human, what

You pray for the right things and God has to grant them to you. Thus pray for strength and wisdom and love and compassion to go through life with grace, humour and positive surrender. That is the best prayer.

you nurture and how you live with a situation decides where you stand spiritually and with your Master."

Both the men stood up. The beach was still deserted. It was getting a little warm. The monsoons were late by more than a fortnight already. Certain parts of the country were already facing acute water shortage. If the monsoons were not up to the mark this year, the situation all over the country could become critical. Rudra dreaded having to read about poor farmers committing suicide, due to a poor monsoon.

They walked to the cottage. Rudra entered the kitchen to make their second cup of tea. He switched on the toaster. Baba liked eating hot toast with melted butter on it. He ate like a child. Rudra loved watching Baba eat. It gave him the same satisfaction as he used to get seeing his children eat. For the first time in years, Rudra enjoyed shopping for fruits and food and then cooking some strange dish with love and anticipation. He used to cook for his kids. Make soups and fruit juices and salads and sandwiches. Then he would sit in front of his kids and watch them eat. They would sit together and talk and laugh and bullshit or watch great movies or serials and just be together. Forgotten to the outside world and in bliss with each other. Since they had gone he had no taste on his tongue. Everything tasted the same; like dust. Nothing mattered. Nothing.

But now with Baba with him, the cross felt lighter, breath flowed easier, nights were shorter. Yes, when alone, he missed the kids even more. When Baba went for his walks or just disappeared for hours, Rudra would often feel his loss and the loss of his children even more intensely. But being around Baba, feeding him, taking

care of him, pressing his feet, preparing his bath or
chillum, made him feel lighter, more alive, less prone to
committing suicide. Taking care of Baba made him feel
as though he was taking care of his children. Also, he
no longer had the craving to drink. In fact, the only
time he did drink was when he went out for a lonely
meal and knew that for the next few hours Baba would
be gone. So he would consume a draft beer, not more
than two glasses and be done with it. The need for
intoxication was no longer fierce.

"Rudra, feed an old man some breakfast and slowly
kill him with that ghastly tea, my child."

"Yeah, yeah." Rudra smiled and heard himself
chuckle.

"LET ME TELL you a secret." They were walking on
the beach after a dinner of fresh, home-made yogurt,
spicy roasted potatoes, whole wheat bread, fresh salads
with lots of chillies and variety of pickles. Then Rudra
had cut fresh mangoes for Baba. Rudra had stopped
eating mangoes. The fruit reminded him of too many
happy times with his children and each morsel choked
him and since years he had stopped eating the fruit.
Baba who never ate or drank anything, without insisting
Rudra partake of it, did not even once suggest Rudra
eat the mango with him. Rudra was not surprised. Baba
knew Rudra's deepest thoughts, even those that were
buried in his subconscious mind.

Rudra had to stop walking, so as to be able to read
Baba's lips and observe the hand movement. It wasn't a
full moon night, two more nights for that, but the beams

were strong and clear, as not a cloud lurked in the sky.

"The secret is simple. God does not take too kindly to those who fight over Him or fight in His name. He does not like people arguing and abusing one another because of Him; over His merits, form and philosophy. It is really a bad idea to kill another human being in His name or in the name of religion or spirituality. You are asking for serious repercussions that could last for lifetimes. But you know what, the worst possible thing you can do is to use His name for manipulating gullible people. These so-called God-men and spiritual leaders and priests of all religions, who use God and His name, and in His name mislead people to commit crimes and kill and riot and turn fanatical; these so-called leaders are in such serious trouble, I cannot begin describing you the lifetimes of hell that await them. There is no greater sin than misusing your evolution; I mean, after reaching a certain state of evolution and spirituality and then misusing your power... misusing your spiritual power, financial power, the power of your position, your charismatic powers... In the name of God and abusing

The more you lose yourself, the more you connect with your Master. The more you shed away yourself, the more space your Master gets to occupy. The less of you means more of your Master within you. Those who are really fine-tuned with their Master's frequency may in the end lose themselves completely and it is in them, their Master or their God reside. Then they become the true vessels or instruments where whatever they say, think, do, see, hear, all is through their Master, in fact it is done by their Master.

those who come to you or look up to you, to be the extension or the voice of God and all that which God stands for and then be abused, physically, financially, emotionally and, worst of all, spiritually. You must have heard about the soul having to go through more than millions of lifetimes to evolve into a human being. Then as a human being, you keep being born again and again till you become so entwined with God and Master that you no longer even breathe without being aware of the presence of God within you. So imagine the innumerable lifetimes an average soul has to go through, first of all to enter the human race and then once as a human being, to relinquish all that which is ungodly and be filled with His light and aura. The soul has to go through every experience and then evolve above it and then move on and go through another experience and conquer it with grace and after every experience and emotion is scaled with positive surrender and grace, the soul is ready to move permanently in the spirit world and become a co-worker or a guide or become an angel to help those in need of God's word and presence.

"Now imagine a person has virtually reached the stage where he or she has outgrown or evolved to the point where there are no longer experiences needed to test his or her spirituality or soul growth. Nature has invested lifetimes in preparing the soul to reach that level. Now imagine, such a person, using his or her spirituality or position of power and begin to abuse or manipulate or even kill. Imagine a highly evolved person using his or her strengths and position and spirituality and charisma to incite people to kill or rape or plunder, all in the name of God. Remember, this person has the power to do so, as he or she has been equipped by nature to tower over other mortals. The person has reached a stage in spiritual growth that empowers the person with different strengths and powers to be able to make others do what he or she wills. Instead of using his or her power for good, the person in the name of God or humanity or charity or leadership begins to abuse and manipulate and becomes the cause of grief and death; how do you think providence or nature or God feel then? Trust me, the heavens feel let down! In what way then, does the law of karma work? Well, the person has to start from scratch once again. Start off from where the soul begins its first tentative steps; as a single cell and then once again go through the hundred of thousands of different life forms to reach mankind. But there is a difference. The soul knows it has done wrong and the inherent character of that soul is that of sadness and it feels the burden of its downfall and misdeeds. It carries a heavy cross but does not know why. All through its journey, it carries inherent sadness but cannot pin it down to the actual reason. This is the law of karma working. For the next hundreds of years, the soul goes through the burden of knowing it has messed up really bad but how-why-what it does not know and will never be able to decipher.

"Remember, killing is a sin. But when a person has reached so close to God and then kills out of anger or revenge or, worse, in a cold calculated way, using his gifts that nature has bestowed on him or her, and that too using God's name, the murder takes on different dimensions. It's as bad as a surgeon killing those very patients who have entrusted their lives to him or her.

The patient, in fact has willingly agreed to be cut up, in the firm belief that the doctor and surgeon knows best and is ideally equipped to do what is in the overall interest and good of the patient. Imagine the surgeon, in a cold calculated manner, killing the unconscious patient who even in death believes that the surgeon knows best. Those in power have the same sway over the masses or those who work for them and who serve them. Misleading or abusing such innocent trusting souls, you are asking for serious trouble with deadly repercussions. We believe that abusing anybody who serves you, or trusts your judgment or taking advantage of those less privileged than you, or being a tyrant to those who serve in any manner, is asking for trouble. That is why I feel sad for those who abuse in the name of God and religion. These politicians, these God men, these so called spiritual leaders and spiritual statesmen, who in the name of God or religion or spirituality abuse and misuse all that which is godly and pure are awaiting hard times. Maybe not in this lifetime but trust me, each lifetime is but a wink of an eye. Being in limbo, not on earth but not in the spirit world, is a nightmare of gigantic proportions and after that having to start from scratch is hell a million times over. All those who wield power of any sort; be it politics, religion, at work, at home, wherever, need to tread carefully and tenderly, as misusing the power they have been given by providence is very harmful for the soul and justice is meted out very harshly later on. As I have told you often, your very soul keeps account and track of all your transgressions, of body, mind and heart. It also keeps track of all the righteous and noble deeds. Then it decides what is best for your spiritual growth and the soul is a hard taskmaster. A very hard taskmaster."

THE RAINS ARRIVED one hot muggy afternoon. Baba and Rudra sat on the veranda and saw the heaven unleash a fury of water down on a parched mother earth. The sea took on a dark brooding colour that looked beautiful. The sky became pregnant with clouds of various hues; dull but enchanting. The fragrance of the earth was mesmerizing. The coconut trees swayed and the various potted plants and flowers seemed to have got a new lease of life.

"This my son, all around you, is something only earth can offer; not even heaven. Every creation of God is filled with certain exclusivity, a rare individuality about it that is not found elsewhere. Earth has a certain uniqueness not found even in the heavens. The joy in seeing the rains fall on parched soil and the immediate grateful response from everything in nature is something exclusive to our planet earth. Look at the way the earth responds to the rain. Even if you were to shut your eyes you could feel the change in all of nature. Look at the way all of creation responds to the first rays of the sun. Nature does not take the gifts that God bestows with

The most effective prayer is to ask God and Master, to endow you with the strength and wisdom, love and compassion, to go through life and its experiences with grace, humour and positive surrender. If you ask for these qualities God has to grant them to you.

indifference. It does not even take it as its birthright. Every morning nature responds joyfully, gratefully, and humbly. But look at human beings, how indifferent most of us are to the bounties of God and nature. When was the last time you thanked God for a beautiful sunrise or rejoiced with nature over the break of dawn? When was the last time you thanked God for giving you the opportunity to live another day and thank the Sun for giving you its light and warmth? When was the last time you thanked God for allowing you to drink the cool, thirst-quenching liquid, which though it has no taste and no colour still has a quality that nothing else has; the ability of quenching your thirst every single time you consume it. Tell me, do you thank God when you drink water? No. Why? Because you take it as your birthright and you take water for granted. But see the way an animal or a bird drinks water. There is a sense of gratitude. Not verbal, but observe and you will see that there is focus and single-minded concentration. You know why boy? Because they are not certain when next will they be able to acquire this nectar of life. Thus, every time they have water there is a sense of gratitude to nature and God above."

Baba then lit the *chillum*. He had a few drags from it and passed it on to Rudra, who did the same. They looked at the heavens pour in torrents and observed nature respond. Yeah, Rudra thought, we all are a part of each other. All of nature is independent but yet entwined. Intertwined by the same life force that pulsates through all of us, all of nature.

Two dogs had walked up the stairs to their bungalow and uncertainly made the veranda their transit home.

One of them was a lovely shade of brown. It was well fed and looked robust. The other had black and white in patches. It was obviously, the brown one's friend and Man Friday, for it allowed the brown one to choose the best spot and then chose one for itself. Rudra stood up and left the veranda. After a while he returned with two plastic bowls that once had served as restaurant take away packs. In them, he had crushed biscuits of different types. He placed them in front of the two dogs and then returned to Baba, who continued to smoke the *chillum* but with a smile that spoke of approval and warmth. The rain poured and in the background they heard loud and happy munching.

It was like some strange music. Raindrops falling, breeze blowing, birds chirping and two dogs busy munching away. Rudra had not heard such pleasing music for a long time.

RUDRA RETURNED FROM the restaurant, with his heart pounding like some tribal drum. His stomach felt knotted but strangely his breath flowed slowly, with a rhythm of its own. What he had experienced with the businessman was nothing but absurd. He was certain, the businessman, a Mr. Seth, would also conclude the same.

My son you are in the moment and when in the moment, you are with the same current that flows through the Lord. You are swimming in the same lake where the Good Lord is swimming too. You are going to be cleansed and purified with the water that has touched the Lord Almighty. That is why it is so important to be in the moment.

Baba only would return from his daily vanishing act in the evening, which gave Rudra enough time to read one of his many unfinished novels as well as gaze at the Arabian Sea. The sky was pregnant with dark melancholy clouds and was virtually waiting to open up and drench mother earth with her downpour. A few minutes after he had settled himself on the old but comfortable sofa that Baba and he had dragged on to the veranda, the rain came gushing down. Rudra hoped Baba was safe. The old man disappeared for hours on certain days and Rudra knew better than inquire as to Baba's gypsy-like excursions. Wherever Baba was, Rudra was certain that he was safe.

The veranda was about ten meters long and five meters wide. It faced the beach and the sea. The roof was tarred and slanted downwards, thus protecting all those who relaxed on the veranda from rain and sun. Just outside the veranda were planted numerous coconut trees and bushes and other flora that Rudra knew nothing about but nonetheless appreciated and they were in abundance. The gate that opened to the beach was fifty feet away and thus the trees and bushes and the flora that Rudra knew nothing about screened the cottage from prying eyes. Fortunately there were no prying eyes, this time of the year. Rudra gazed at the sea. The waves came in torrents and the sea resembled a herd of wild animals, running in all directions, beautiful, untamed and lethal. The sky had turned black and the wind blew with a raging fury.

Rudra lit a cigarette and for a long time sat mesmerized by the entire drama of nature that enfolded in front of him. It would have been perfect if his children were with him now. He would have held them and they would have talked and joked and asked him to narrate the fascinating stories of Lord Rama or Lord Hanuman or the oldest known Prophet known to mankind, Prophet Zarathushtra, who gave the world Zoroastrianism, and who preached sometime in 3000 B.C. that there was only one God and that God (Ahura Mazda) had no form but was Omnipotent, Omnipresent, All-knowing, infinitely noble and absolutely a cool dude. Of course, miracles performed by Sai Baba of Shirdi and Meher Baba never ceased to fascinate his children. He missed their small warm fingers on his face; his son's head resting on Rudra's chest; his daughter cuddling and massaging his arms and pinching his cheeks; their round bodies and their fragrance, that was a strange mix of Johnson Baby powder and some soap and some detergent used for their clothes and of course their own body fragrance... Rudra breathed in deep and shut his eyes and with focus on his breathing, got his children out of his mind. Of course, the mind he could control. But the kids reigned in his heart and had a strong hold on his soul and thrashed him nice and good in his subconscious. For two hours he read a little and stared at the sea. After a while the rain subsided but the vast

"Chanting of prayers and mantras is like putting fuel to a spiritual fire. Like when we do a *havan*, a fire ceremony. We are saying our prayers and we keep adding sandalwood or fuel to the holy fire. What takes place? What started off as a small flame, through the wood and the fuel and all other things that are offered, helps the flame become a raging and roaring fire."

sea in front of him remained rough and beckoning. All he had to do was walk into it. Just keep walking. Maybe he would have to swallow a huge amount of salt water but what the hell, all would be over in a few minutes. He had withstood hours of absolute torture watching badly made Hindi movies and ghastly cartoons a thousand times, with his kids. A few minutes of agony while committing suicide seemed child's play.

His thoughts once again returned to the businessman. Rudra still could not comprehend why he had spoken to the stranger and from where the words had flowed. All he knew was that the businessman had turned white initially and nearly passed out but then was very interested.

Rudra lit another cigarette. He did not consume much liquor any more. It just didn't seem right to drink in front of Baba. But when Baba was out on his spiritual jaunts, Rudra would consume a few draft beers before lunch, smoke a few cigarettes, read all the while and then eat some grilled food. He could no longer consume normal food. His system was slowly closing up on him. The nerves in his head were slowly getting damaged and there was no cure for it. As he often told himself, all in all, he was burning both ends of the candle and it was the surest and darnest way of hastening his exit without actually pulling the trigger and ending his miserable life.

Today, after Baba had left, around noon, Rudra walked to the small restaurant by the sea, run by a Goan couple that provided the best possible grilled food but who ran the establishment like a military school. They did not smile, their waiters seemed abrupt and the entire place lacked the fun and frolic that is usually associated with Goan Christian owned restaurants all over the country. What the Martin's lacked in hospitality and warmth was compensated by the most delicious food dished up in their kitchen. Maybe the cooks had warmth and joviality cruising through their veins and thus the food tasted so darn delicious. The pricing was another strong point for the popularity of the restaurant. It was very reasonable and thus Martin's was always bursting at its seams. Any time of the day and way into the night, the crowds thronged to eat and drink and gaze at the sea. You had folks from all over the world having a go at their food, but religiously avoiding the eyes of the dour man sitting at the counter or the missus who could easily manhandle a few thugs with one hand while the other hand pointed directions to those who wanted a seat in her establishment. The waiters looked at you with polite disgust and a smile that hoped you'd rot in hell but not through food poisoning. Very often one had to hesitate to ask the waiter to perform some task that was not in the immediate 'to do' list of the dreary man. But the food was good, beer fresh, view excellent and the prices just right. All you had to take care of in this crazy joint was avoid making eye contact with those

This fire provides you warmth, nourishment, strength, light and eternal life. As you keep chanting, all the secrets of the universe enfold and stand before you, as nothing can be hidden from the light. As you keep chanting, you become part of the fire and then you become the fire itself and through this process you, the divine light, merge with the Eternal Fire and Light. It is very simple actually.

who ran this establishment and those who worked for the place; then all was well with the world.

Rudra had just finished ordering his beer and grilled chicken when this man walked up to him and apologetically inquired if he could share the table with him, as he was in a hurry and nobody seemed inclined to be anywhere close to completing their meal. Rudra nodded in the affirmative and gazed at the waters lashing the rocks that were a few metres away from the restaurant. He had been calm since morning and made certain that neither depression nor thoughts about his children assailed his heart and mind. It was sheer emptiness that made him feel light and virtually at peace with himself and with the world.

Rudra looked at the man seated opposite him. He was middle-aged, with white sideburns, a brief case and two mobile phones. The man had switched both of them off knowing the repercussions could be damaging. Either one of the Martins would have wrung his neck or jumped on the phones with their spiked shoes. The Martins did not want to encourage idle chat. 'Eat your darn food and bugger off' being the unmentioned but obvious underlying philosophy of the Martin clan. So mobile phones were a certain no-no. The man had a faraway look that spoke clearly that life was giving him the thrashing of his life. Rudra was familiar with that look. He had seen it in his eyes countless times. Thus he avoided the mirror if possible. For some reason Rudra prayed for the man. Prayed that he find peace and strength. He prayed that whatever was troubling him either be sorted out or God give him the strength and wisdom to go through the ordeal. Seconds after he had finished saying the prayer, suddenly the weird things started.

Rudra heard himself speak to the man. He had no intention of beginning a conversation. He did not want to talk to anybody, least of all a stranger. But here he was speaking to the man about things he had no clue about. The conversation went something like this...

"Don't worry all will go well. They will accept your proposal. They will try to bring down your profit margin but don't give in. What you've asked for is right. Even the bank will pass the loan after you get the approval. Just remember not to make the same mistakes and stay away from the stock market. If you don't you will be on the street and you will make your family miserable. Don't worry about your daughter, she will leave that office soon and once she leaves it the affair with that man will automatically end. Get her married once she completes her twenty-sixth birthday and yes, once your deal comes through and you are settled, keep five per cent of your profit for charity. Remember that every time you make hundred rupees; keep aside five rupees for the poor. If you make five million dollars then keep five per cent of that for the poor.'

For a few seconds, both the men sat stunned. Rudra certainly more shocked than the businessman. Then the questions began.

"How you knowing about all this? How you knowing that I have submitted a proposal? How you

As you keep chanting the Holy Name, the fire keeps growing.

knowing that I have lost all in speculation in the stock market? Who telling you about my daughter having a relationship with her boss who is twenty years her senior?"

Rudra gulped. He could feel the tremor in his fingers. He could feel his heart thud away like a drum out of control. He could sense his breathing but surprisingly that seemed regular and in perfect harmony.

"I don't know. I'm sorry. I don't know..."

"NO! NO! All that you've telling me is true. Yes I am waiting faar order to being approved from America. If that being passed I am safe and I beginning my life again. If I nat getting cantract I being finished. My family and I being on street. All this happening because my madness faar staack market. I have laast everything; everything in my greed to earn more and more. If I getting this cantract, then the banks having assured me they will back me up. I pramise that I will keep aside five per cent for the poor..."

"Your grandmother used to help the blind..."

"MY GOD!" The businessman stood up and then sat down slowly. "How do you knowing all this? Yes, my granny used to being helping those ladies who being nearly blind but who could be saved through aperations and medications. So she would spansor the aperations and taking care of the cast. I will also doing that. Yes I will doing that. I will start a small trust on her name and keeping five per cent of what I make..."

"Five per cent of your profit. Net profit."

"I pramise to do that..."

"You'd better or you'll not only come on the streets but blindness will strike somebody very close to you..."

"NO! NO! I will keep my word. And about my daaghter, I will making her leave her job. But she not agreeing…"

"Send her abroad to handle your work…"

Tears began to flow down the man's cheeks. Rudra saw a grown up man weep but they were tears of gratitude.

"Yes. She has always wanting to being go abroad. She will agreeing then. I will. Who are you? How you knowing all this? Tell me?"

Rudra had already lost his appetite by then. He stood up, called the waiter who came with a frown writ large on his small forehead.

"Cancellation of orders is not permitted."

"Yeah! Yeah! I know. Pack the stuff."

"Its already been put on the…"

"Pack the freaking stuff man." The waiter recoiled. Rudra had visited the place often. He did not seem like a man with a spark of anger in him. All of a sudden the waiter realized that there was a volcano brewing within and he nodded hastily and left.

"My name is Seth. Please telling me where can I cantact you. Please. And when will the arder come…"

"Fourteen days from today."

"Where can I meet you? PLEASE!" A few diners had begun to look at the two men with interest. Obviously the one with two phones was visibly excited and in complete awe of the younger man. But the latter, with long hair and a four-day stubble, was in a state of shock and bewilderment. Whatever was happening was out of the ordinary.

"Please understand, I myself don't know what is

happening. I don't know why or what I spoke to you. Maybe it was God's way of helping you out..."

"My friend I was going to be borrowing money on such a high rate of interest that it would having broken my back. The fact that you have being talking about the U.S. arder without knowing anything, has given me great hope. Or else I would have barrowing money in the evening and from whom I being barrowing money are very bad. They would have made me signing all my property and business as guarantee. With the money I was going to dabbling on the staack market. You know if I doing that and I then loosing that I being finished. Only suicide my way being out. And you have showing me a way out for my daaghter too. Thank you." Then the man did something that spooked Rudra. He bent and touched Rudra's feet. A few people turned. Martin frowned. The waiter froze. Rudra exhaled. The waiter handed Rudra his food and Rudra walked out of the restaurant in a daze. Absolutely unaware of what had transpired; what or how or why.

Seated now on the veranda, Rudra was still in a daze. How could he have known all those things about a stranger? How? And what had compelled him to speak out? Whatever had taken place was beyond his control. Of that he was certain. As certain as seeing the sun set on the water this very moment. After a few seconds Rudra smiled. As certain as seeing the sun set on the water? That was an illusion man. The sun didn't set. It did not rise. It did not move about everyday from the east to the west. It was planet earth that did all the movement but it sure seemed the sun did the prancing about. Yeah, life was one grand illusion. Darkness and night did not settle onto a place because the sun had set but because that part of planet earth had shown its back to the sun.

"The same way, my young boy, who goes about predicting the future to strangers and spooking the pants off them, God never moves away but the individual does and shows his or her back to God and when you show your back to God then darkness engulfs you. That is what the good Lord is trying to show us all through the sun and the earth and the moon and all of nature. Though everything is an illusion it is also there for a purpose. When the earth shows it back to the sun, the night then falls. In a similar way, darkness, confusion, pain, loneliness enters the individual's life, when he or she turns away from God and not because God has moved away. God is the Sun. The individual is planet earth. If you turn your back to God then there is darkness in your life, son. So the best is to keep moving towards God. Be in the light forever. Now come let's have that ghastly tea and tell me all about how you have become an expert in predicting stuff for folks who have come to eat some badly made food by that military run restaurant you keep visiting. Ha! Ha!"

Rudra smiled and began to chuckle along. Nothing about the old man surprised him anymore.

I am always by your side, when you think of me. If you want me by your side every moment, then simply think about me every moment.

"BABA, TELL ME what happened at Martin's?" They had finished having their mint tea and sandwiches. Baba ate very frugally. But at night, he barely ate more than a slice or two of sandwiches that Rudra made at home. Sometimes Baba did not eat even that. Yes, he loved to have tea and Rudra prepared lots of it, all through the day. Before he went to sleep, Rudra would prepare enough to fill up at least one thermos with piping hot mint tea.

Baba spent the major part of the night in prayer. He would sit in the bedroom, in front of the many oil lamps and candles and pray. His fingers would keep moving and sometimes his hands would make gestures. Rudra would sleep on the other side of the room and observe this old man, full of kindness and power, pray and meditate on the Holy Fire, till sleep engulfed Rudra in her shadowy snare. So often, when Rudra would awaken, he would find Baba seated in the same position, lips moving softly, gazing lovingly into the flames, with light and darkness making different patterns on the white walls. Rudra would often, then, slowly sit up and wait. After a while, Baba would inevitably turn towards him and smile. Rudra loved that smile. It brought tears to his eyes, seeing the love and tenderness in that smile. Rudra would then gesticulate, if Baba would like to drink a cup of tea or *chai*.

So often, Baba and Rudra would sit in the cozy room of theirs, sipping tea, observing the flames throw gentle glimmers through the otherwise dark room. If ever Rudra was close to caressing heaven, these were the moments. Whether they drank tea or not, if Rudra was awake, for a while he would make Baba lie down and then Rudra would press Baba's feet and legs. Baba experienced severe pain in the feet and calves. Sometimes the nerves were stretched and rigid. Often, when Baba would come from his spiritual excursions, Rudra would realize his nerves were in the worst possible shape. Baba slept for a few hours in the night. In fact, Rudra had never seen Baba really sleep. The old sage lay with eyes shut but he never really slept. So often, with eyes shut, Baba would answer a query that Rudra had only thought about, leave aside, spoken aloud.

"The tea today is excellent. How come?"

"Very funny Baba. Tell me, please, what happened today!"

Baba prepared his *chillum*. It was a slow process and sometimes, Rudra felt, it was more of a spiritual process, as though, Baba was preparing himself, filling himself up with some strange spiritual energy, before answering Rudra's never-ending queries. So Rudra sat and watched the sea. The beams of the moon fell on the darkish silvery water and the sound of the waves was soothing. Rudra would be heartbroken to leave this place. The money would last them a few more months. At least, the monsoons could be spent in this safe haven. The cottage was named Dwarka. Rudra's Guru, Sai Baba of Shirdi,

Son we all are entwined in karma and in God. Don't hurt or hate or abuse anybody as you don't know, you may be hurting your dearest and most beloved, but you can't recognize it as the soul is wearing a different body in this particular lifetime.

had spent His life in a dilapidated Masjid (a place of worship for Moslems), and named the Masjid, Dwarkamai.

"Let me ask you a few questions and then I will answer yours!" Baba gesticulated. Rudra nodded an affirmative. "Have you been doing all that I have been telling you to do?"

"Yes. Everything." It began raining. Rudra stood up, left the veranda and returned with a shawl, that he draped around Baba.

"What have you been doing?"

"First of all, the mind is either engrossed in the moment or I chant a prayer. "

"What do you mean engrossed in the moment?"

"Exactly what you have taught me Baba. If I am eating food, I enjoy the whole process of eating. My entire attention and also my entire gratitude, is merged with the process of eating. I am not doing it mechanically or grudgingly. I also invite God to share the meal and the experience and virtually with every morsel, I thank Him for the food. Through the process, my thoughts also have gone to those who are starving and automatically a short prayer goes out into the universe for all those hungry and dying of hunger; with the belief that the energy and conviction with which I have prayed for them will make a positive difference to their lives or at least to a few lives."

"How?"

"The prayer will create an energy that will influence a few people to share their food with the poor. For instance, the prayers will influence some kind soul to stop the car and hand a packet of biscuits or fruits or something to eat to the beggar standing on the signal or the prayer might influence a kind soul to donate money or bags of grain to a charity that takes care of those in need of food and sustenance. Or my short prayer might give some poor person strength to go through the difficult period of hunger. In the sense, the vibrations created by the prayer might give a poor person the calmness to accept his or her lot with grace and positive surrender. All these things are hoped for before I eat food. Very often with every morsel I eat. I know how blessed I am not to feel the pangs of hunger and not to worry where my next morsel comes from. I know that Baba. You know I have gone through hunger. You know I have searched my house for a few coins to feed my kids and family. I have seen those days, Baba, and I know you are aware of it all. Thus I know what it is not to have food and see your children and loved ones go hungry. I know and thus I feel. May be to feel I had to know and go through the experience and thus become a channel for prayers and vibrations. Whatever the case be, I know what it is to be ravaged by hunger. I never forget. I also never forget how Sai Baba of Shirdi always

A person who you think hates you or wants to finish you off and in return you hate, might be you're your greatest well-wisher spiritually. He or she may be responsible for your turning spiritual or compassionate. That very person who is creating hell in your life may bring you closer to God and prayers and spirituality but is doing so in a manner that hurts you in the present lifetime, but maybe, that is the only way you will learn the lesson.

maintains that all those who take the Name of God and Master never starve. They need never worry about food and clothes. Never. I believe this. Whatever my situation was, food would arrive at the last moment. From some place and somewhere money to buy food would arrive."

"I know my son. I am aware. It's good you understand that you had to go through the process of pain and experience of hunger so that you could be compassionate towards all those who seek food, for themselves or their family. Nature knew you would convert the experiences of hunger to a higher goal... for a higher purpose. You would pray for the poor and the starving. You would make people help those who are starving. That is how the sacred link works. Nature and Providence do not get some quaint satisfaction in seeing any living being suffer or agonize but They do have a higher purpose in mind and hope that the being embraces the higher purposes and deals with adversity calmly and with grace.

"You know son, the most effective prayer is to ask God and Master, to endow you with the strength and wisdom, love and compassion, to go through life and its experiences with grace, humour and positive surrender. If you ask for these qualities God has to grant them to you. Don't ask for anything else, as that may not be in your destiny to receive. For example, you might be destined to go through certain experiences; for example, experiences of ill health. For some karmic reason, you have to go through ill health for a few years, let us say, from the age of thirty-five to forty-two you are destined to go through health issues, and God and Nature, hope that you will learn what you have to and then move on and not be put through the experience again. Now if you keep praying for good health, day and night; take the best medicines; get treated by the most reputed and efficient doctors; have the ideal diet and lifestyle; still, if you have to go through the phase of ill health, then you will go through that phase, come what may. So by praying for good health, it is not going to be of much help. But if you pray for strength and wisdom, love and compassion, to go through your ill health and all that which your God, Master and destiny have in store for you, with grace, humour and positive surrender, then your prayers have to be granted. Thus though you may have ill health, you will be blessed with strength and wisdom to go through that phase with grace and dignity; you will be able to face the illness with humour and most important of all, you will deal with the illness with positive and graceful surrender as the will of God and Master. You will be ill but will not suffer and most important, you learn from the experience and come out a more compassionate human being who will then feel and empathize with the sick and the damned. You will also begin to help the sick and the ailing. Thus, you will be able to convert the experience to a higher good and a larger spiritual purpose. You will not turn into a negative and angry human being who might despise God and those blessed with good health. All this is possible because you have prayed and

Sometimes an opportunity comes in the form of a disaster. Sometimes the only way God can find place in your heart and life is through pain and sorrow and turmoil.

asked God for the right things. You pray for the right things and God has to grant them to you. Thus, pray for strength and wisdom and love and compassion to go through life with grace, humour and positive surrender. That is the best prayer. Now back to you. What is important is that through the entire process you should enjoy whatever your are doing or at least be at peace with whatever you are involved with!"

"Yes, I am trying to…"

"Good. And this kind of involvement, you are trying to keep up with all that you do?'

"Yeah. It has come to a situation that today while walking towards that silly Martin's restaurant, an ambulance passed me and a prayer left my soul for whosoever the ambulance was meant for. Not only for the person who was sick, but a prayer passed my lips that God give strength of emotion and finance, to all those who are directly or indirectly going to be affected by the ailment or accident. Baba, the prayer happened on its own…"

"That is because, my son, you are in the moment and when in the moment, you are with the same current that flows through the Lord. You are swimming in the same lake where the Good Lord is swimming too. You are going to be cleansed and purified with the water that has touched the Lord Almighty. That is why it is so important to be in the moment. If you weren't in the moment, the ambulance would have passed by without your prayer and your vibrations. Remember, whatever you think and wish for, is heard and felt and accepted by nature and nature does turn it into energy. Now it can be good energy or negative. It all depends upon each individual. Imagine, millions of individuals wishing good and sending positive thoughts and feelings and thus creating an ocean of positive vibrations. These vibrations spread through the universe influencing all of creation. It's like entering into a room that was lived in by a couple that was filled with hatred for each other or the world. The moment you enter the room you feel horrid and creepy and despondent. That energy, you carry with you and it does influence you in your actions and thoughts, even if temporarily. Now, enter a room that is inhabited by a family that loves each other and enjoys life and prays and works for the larger good. Automatically you feel great. You feel warm and happy. Compassionate. You carry these positive feelings with you for a while. These positive emotions influence you to be good and be more charitable and forgiving and compassionate, even if it is just for a while.

"Even if it is for a short period of time. Now imagine the world filled with those who love God and who nurture compassion for all the living in their soul. Can you imagine the vibrations emitted and transmitted? It shall influence millions of people and if the energy is consistent and perpetual, the influence too will be consistent and persistent and perpetual. It shall influence more good, which shall create more positive energy and

The Guru is all knowing, my son, and the Guru knows what is best for His or Her child. The Guru knows at what speed the child has to travel and how heavy the cross should be and how fast the karmic cleansing should be. Leave it all to your Guru. The Guru knows best and knows it all.

the cycle will perpetuate itself for eternity. It is a fact. But enjoy the moment. Don't begrudge it. Don't get all serious and fussy. Be cool and live it with a light heart. But there will be times when you might not be able to focus on the moment. What do you then?"

"Those times I chant the name of God and my Masters. But whosoever fills me up at that moment. It could be Shiv, Rama, Ganesha, Krishna, Hanuman, Ma Mookambika, Kali Ma, Jesus and Mary, Zarathustra, Allah, Guru Nanak, Makdum Shah, Sai Baba of Shirdi or Meher Baba. Whosoever fills me up at that moment, the name fills my soul. So when I can't focus on the moment and I know that my mind is going to create hell, I begin chanting God's name. And I have realized that chanting Their names really has protected me from negative thoughts and unnecessary pain and anxiety. Earlier, I used to be in the present moment as a form of escapism. Not to think about my kids I would hide in the present moment. But now I enjoy being in the present moment. I am not hiding behind the present moment but I am just flowing with the present moment. And when I can't flow with it, I begin to chant my prayers."

"Chanting of prayers and mantras is like putting fuel to a spiritual fire. Like when we do a *havan*, a fire ceremony. We are saying our prayers and we keep adding sandalwood or fuel to the holy fire. What takes place? What started off as a small flame, through the wood and the fuel and all other things that are offered, helps the flame become a raging and roaring fire. So the same reaction takes place with consistent prayers and chanting of mantras or just repeating your God or Master's name. Initially it is just a small flame or flicker of light. But as you keep repeating the sacred words or Name, then slowly the spark becomes a small flame, which becomes a tiny fire, which after regular feeding of fuel or in this case regular chanting of the Name, helps the tiny spark to grow into a raging fire. As you keep chanting the Holy Name, the fire keeps growing. This fire that burns within your soul, dispels darkness and negativity. It destroys and burns away all your past karma. It shows you the way. It keeps all darkness away from you. It enlightens you with knowledge that you never thought existed, as earlier it was hidden in the layers of darkness that initially engulfed you but now has been burnt away, by the raging fire that burns within; lighting up everything around you. This fire provides you warmth, nourishment, strength, light and eternal life. As you keep chanting, all the secrets of the universe unfold and stand before you, as nothing can be hidden from the light. As you keep chanting, you become part of the fire and then you become the fire itself and through this process you, the divine light, merge with the Eternal Fire and Light. It is very simple actually. It requires no fancy training. Just be in the moment and be true to yourself. Chant the name of your God and Master or say your prayer but say it with honesty, love and concentration. It is very simple this process. Leave all to God and Master and give your best to life... more important, give your best to the moment. Parmahansa Yoganda has said it, so beautifully, in *The Autobiography of A Yogi...*"God

The intention of the soul is more important than all the earthly laws put together.

is simple, everything else is complex". That is the eternal truth. God does not need anything complex or elaborate. He wants love and simplicity and honesty. All He wants is to throb in your soul. Now relax. We will talk about what happened tomorrow. Go have some dinner. Go out. Enjoy life..."

"You are my life Baba."

Tears welled in the young man's eyes. Baba breathed in deep and then whispered a short prayer. They sat for a while and took in the majesty of the sea.

"Why can't I come along Baba? I can take care of things for you. Make you my ghastly tea and when you're tired I can press your feet. Come on, let me come too."

Baba smiled and continued to pack his meagre belongings. He sat down on the soft sofa and held Rudra's hand and softly tugged the younger man to sit down beside him.

"I'm going away for a few days; nothing to get worried or sad about. Most importantly, I am never going to leave you. I have been with you for many lifetimes and whether you were or are aware of it, I am always by your side, when you think of me. If you want me by your side every moment, then simply think about me every moment. The more you do that the stronger our bond. But even when you don't think about me, my energy surrounds you, enveloping you in my love. So worry not. Worry never, as I am here, with you, always."

For the next two days Rudra did not leave the cottage. He sat near the cot that Baba lay on, and made sure

that the flames that Baba had lit kept burning bright.
Strangely, Rudra did feel Baba's presence next to him.
The room in which they slept had a few windows, but
Rudra always made certain that the bright sunlight was
kept at bay. Thus the room took on the look of a cave:
lamps burning throughout; semi darkness through the
day and deep darkness through the night, only the flames
and the shadows they created dancing on the walls.
Rudra realized that he did spend most of his time
chanting the Holy Name.

A week later, one night, he realized, that even though
sound asleep, when he had stirred for a few seconds to
shift his body's position, the Holy Name, resounded in
his mind and heart. The next morning Rudra realized
the importance of chanting the Holy Name; whatever it
may be, through the day. He recalled what Baba had
talked to him a few days earlier about keeping thoughts
and the mind in check. Baba had said that the mind was
a wonderful creation. Thoughts were attached to the
mind. Like horses are reigned onto a chariot. Either you
controlled thoughts or the thoughts controlled you.
Either you were its Guru or it was your Guru. Like fire,
it could be life-enhancing or it could char you to death.
If you lived in the moment, the mind was occupied. The
Holy Name made certain that the mind, when not in

The stronger and cleaner and purer the individual, the more
powerful and clear, he or she becomes as a vessel or an instrument,
to carry the Holy Word and be filled with the Holy Spirit. It is the
birthright of every living organism, to become the medium and
vessel, for the Lord above.

the moment, was still at home; either swim in the current of the moment, or keep chanting one's God or Master's name; the Holy Name; thus all the time, the mind along with its horses are harnessed with the reigns in one's own hands. What could be better than to live one's life, without being distracted and controlled by thoughts and various issues of the past or anxiety about the future?

Thoughts are like horses. Each thought equivalent to one horse. More thoughts, the chariot (the mind) has more horses. Now imagine each horse wanting to run in a different direction. Ten horses wanting to take a breather, disgusted with the idea of running to and fro. Twenty horses wanting to run to the left, where a stable housed yummy mares. Forty horses wanting to run straight where at a short distance a stream flowed, carrying with it the coolest and most enchanting water. Of course, seventeen horses cared two figs for females or water. They wanted to move to the right where civilization throbbed, as these horses did not think too highly of rural life; they thrived on traffic, city life and the glamour of the neon lights at night. Imagine all the horses determined to carry out their desires. What a nightmare for the chariot driver who obviously has little say in the proceedings. The horses don't care a rat's ass for the chariot or the charioteer; simply because the person who holds the reigns doesn't have it in him or her to control and lead. More often than not, most chariots and charioteers face the same dilemma; too many horses with contrasting agendas thus the journey (life) is really a painful affair. This is also the case with one's mind and the contrasting ruling thoughts. Each horse is a thought. There are innumerable thoughts

crisscrossing through at a given moment. The mind is
the chariot. The individual is the charioteer. With so
many thoughts pulling and tugging to move in a
particular direction and some thoughts, with great
strength and determined stubbornness, insisting on
staying put in one place the journey of life becomes a
nightmare. However strong the chariot may be or skilled
the charioteer, untill all the horses are in unison about
the path and the way through it, only hell and
pandemonium rule. Nothing reigns but chaos. Living
in the present moment and chanting the Holy Name
and walking with the Lord creates a single-minded desire
and a harmonious momentum that makes the journey
blissful and enjoyable. In fact such beautiful unity and
harmony exists, that the numerous horses seem to mould
and merge together and evolve into one robust,
tremendously strong and agile Stallion. This Stallion
gallops as though It possess the road. To manage this
Stallion is child's play. Then the charioteer enjoys the
ride. The chariot comes to no harm, as the danger of
being torn or ripped apart no longer exists. The distance
is covered in the shortest period of time, allowing the
charioteer, the chariot and the Stallion, more time to
relax and enjoy life and this brings about longevity.

Every Holy Book preaches one to pray and meditate; preaches one to
be content and at peace with the plans of the Maker. Why? Because
when you pray and meditate and are at peace and content with your
Lord and Master, then you allow yourself to become a vessel; a
medium; an instrument for the Holy Spirit to enter you.

Rudra realized that the philosophy could all be summed into one sentence: if the horses (thoughts) are under control and they mould into one great Stallion (one focused thought or plan or action), the chariot (the mind) runs smoothly and the charioteer (the individual) has a blast and good health in the journey of life. Simple philosophy but Rudra knew that he would have to work hard and intelligently, to convert those wild horses to see and agree on one common path and have the same goal and thus let him live in peace. One thing he was certain about; the mad herd was converting into a rational breed. He could sense the harmony dawn and he could ascertain the features of the Stallion; hazy picture but nonetheless the Stallion was nearby. 'He better be nearby or I'll have to castrate all those freaking horses myself.'

Rudra avoided the Martin's. The chance meeting with Mr. Seth had really unsettled him. What had transpired two weeks earlier was safely tucked away into the bursting-at-its-seam Compartment of 'Rudra Going Insane'. He concluded that he did not need anything further to complicate his already messed up life. The pain in his head was only getting worse. Obviously, the nerves in his brain were fighting a losing battle, after all the abuse they had been put through, the past few years.

Last night he had dreamt about his children once again. His son was clinging to him and pleading that he not go away. Rudra could still hear the cry in his little boy's voice. It was a dark room and his son was frightened that his mother would come in and see both father and son together, yet the boy kept pleading that no matter how impossible the task, Rudra make some kind of peace and compromise, so that father and son could be together. How does one make peace with somebody who wants a state of war, as it is only in the state of war that all the abuse, manipulations and allegations can be justified? Rudra understood one thing clearly... sometimes hatred was the only wall that protected people from accepting the real state of things. Till they nurtured hatred and thoughts of abuse and revenge, the mind was kept occupied and till the mind was kept occupied, the reality of the situation was kept at bay. Thus, hatred prevented and protected people from accepting their role and guilt and their responsibility of something gone wrong. Thus, in the guise of hatred, some sort of illusionary sanity prevailed. If the hatred and anger disappeared, then there was nothing else to prevent the reality of the situation from seeping in. If hate and hysteria were let go off, then the mind would begin to work on the real cause of what went wrong. Then the individual would have to accept one's role and responsibility for the mess. It takes strength to accept one's fault and it takes courage to accept that one has lied, manipulated and twisted facts, used one's family, friends and worst of all one's very own children to fire a gun; not only used little shoulders to fire but in fact fired the gun through little bodies to hit where it hurts the most! Most people do not have such strength, character or dignity to face reality.

If you empty yourself of all those thoughts and desires and greed and hate and obsessions, automatically the Spirit of the Lord enters you. Remember, in you, only one can reside: you or your Master. There is no place for two to rule.

No matter what fault lay with Rudra, he had never manipulated anybody; never used or abused anybody; never even tried to fight for his name or against all the baseless allegations fired at him. In fact, it was because he had tried to resolve the situation, own up to his mistakes and begin a fresh life, that the present situation prevailed. That he had been tricked on the grounds of 'starting a fresh life' hurt him more than everything else put together. He was no saint but he never once tried to prove that he was not the devil that he was being made out to be. All this in the hope that his children were not further caught in any crossfire. He may have slipped as a man and as a husband but he was not the only one who had slipped. The only difference was that he had kept quiet about what he knew. His reason was simple... the one who had slipped along with him was once part of his life and an integral part of the lives of his children. How does one scream from the rooftop about something as private as that? Can one justify stabbing a pregnant woman and then later claiming that ' my problem was only with the mother and not the child within?'

Rudra sighed. They could keep all their cleverness and their hatred and their petty manipulation and little schemes and their dirty allegations and go about pretending to wear a robe of purity. They could throw their stones and cut him up with their tongues and their parochial intentions. He knew one thing for sure; he would meet his children when they met in the spirit. He would be able to live with his children for eternity in his Father's Home, when they all met after they had dropped their bodies and left this abused planet. He had already paid for his sins by being kept away from his little children. A price that even the most barbaric criminal and murderer did not have to pay...for even the worst terrorist or criminal got a chance to meet his or her family, once in a while in the confines of the cell. So, Rudra had paid his price. He had carried his cross. He had done it quietly. Silently. Without nurturing any hate or malicious schemes. Even now there was no hatred. Sadness? Yes. As Baba often told him, "there is nothing wrong in falling...we all fall...We all have fallen sometime or the other in some life or the other... The important point is not to get crushed, not to bicker, not to hate, not to abuse and be negative to God or the world or those who are trying their best to ruin you... If you succeed in rising above the situation with grace, then son, you have not fallen but actually risen far above what you possibly would and could have, without undergoing the pain and agony. Heaven is not filled with those who have never fallen. It is filled with those who have overcome their circumstances, shortfalls, weakness and most of all, those who have learnt to let go gracefully and leave all the results to Him, the Maker. Heaven is filled with failures, who got to their feet, dusted their clothes, smiled and walked on with God on their lips and heaven in their hearts."

The more you fill yourself up with your Master's name and thought, the more you get filled up with His or Her energy and automatically you become a medium for your Master.

Rudra went for a long walk on the beach. Two weeks had passed and there was no sign of Baba. No, that would be a wrong statement. Two weeks without any physical interaction with Baba. The fact remained that Baba was with Rudra all the time. Rudra could feel the old man's presence. He could sense Baba's energy through the day. It was surreal, this intimacy. It was exhilarating. It was even bizarre. Whatever it was, Rudra loved this connection.

He sat under a palm tree and lit a cigarette. The sky was overcast and he hoped it would not rain. He had no strength to jog to his cottage and no peculiar craving to get drenched. The housework was not much but it was something he had neither interest nor patience for especially when he had to do it for himself and not for Baba. When the old man was with him, Rudra loved doing everything, as he knew it was for the comfort of the sage.

It was so important to love somebody. The very act of loving made life's little chores and dos and don'ts, so worth the while. Only the blessed had the opportunity to really experience true and selfless love. For selfless love not only enhanced the recipient's life but one's own too. Now he understood why mothers love to cook. Why parents work so hard all their lives to provide their children with the best of education, skills and give them all the quality raw material to build a great future on. At least, they try to provide whatever is humanly possible for their little animals, sorry, little children. Love convinces the sun to shine, the earth to revolve, flowers to bloom, seasons to change, crops to grow, art to blossom, babies to gurgle and lovers to sigh. It is God's love for us that makes all the above things possible and keeps our planet from self destructing a million times faster than it really is!

For some odd reason Rudra remembered his close friends. Those who chose to stay by him and those who preferred to walk away. The odd part was that he missed all of them. He missed all those who once loved him and whom he loved. Maybe they were no longer together. Maybe they did not wish him well. Maybe they were angry or hurt with him. But the fact remained, that a small part of his soul died each time a relationship withered away. Be it friend or lover, a small part of him did die with the earthly end of the relationship. Oddly enough, he still loved them, still wished them well, still would do all that was possible to help and protect them. How can one begin to hate somebody one has dearly loved at some point in one's life? To love somebody, anybody, be it man, woman, child, pet, country, religion, whatever, means to have opened one's heart and soul and allowed the energy to blossom within. It means you have given permission to your soul, to allow a piece of you to be possessed and nurtured by that loved one. A part of you and your soul belong to that loved one. If the love was real, there can be no hate. How can one hate the memories of love and laughter and companionship and tenderness? If it was possible, then

As long as a human being tries to walk the path of God; as long as a person wants to walk the path of light; that person is all right; as that person, just with intentions is already on the path. Who are we to judge? Let only the Fakir do the judging.

Rudra was blissfully ignorant about such worldly procedures.

He stood up and began to walk towards his cottage. A few yards away from it, he saw Seth and a young couple waiting for him. He cursed softly. Uttered words, Rudra was certain, would have made Baba laugh aloud. Where was the old mischievous lion, he wondered, not without a smile crinkling his lips and a twinkle sparkling his tired eyes?

Seth immediately touched Rudra's feet. This spooked our man out. He had done nothing to gain such respect. Seth was elder to him and usually the business of feet touching was the prerogative of the young. Or one dived and touched the feet of a Guru; a Master; not necessarily in the wide arena of spirituality but also music, literature, theatre, films, sport, martial art etc.

"Sir, whatever you tellings me is coming true. In America, they signing me and tellings me to open office there and my daughter willing to leave country and beginning work there and…" the man then could go on no further, as tears began to gush down his cheeks and he actually began to sob. Rudra was not very good at handling outbursts, but something within him made him understand Seth's strong emotional outburst and even

Not for a moment should the piano take the credit for the phenomenal music that is created and which flows through it, for it is the Musician that is responsible for the melody.

not get embarrassed by it. "You not knowing if you were not meeting and speaking with me, I would be by now being finished..."

"Mr. Seth, just relax man. I've done nothing. I still don't know how or why, I even spoke to you. Maybe it was God's way of saving you and as God was short staffed on that particular day, he had no option but use me, to help out. I've done nothing and I have no such powers or strengths to repeat the act..."

"You saving me and that's all I knowing but please...please now saving my nephew. Please Rudraji!"

Rudraji. Wow. He felt a hundred years old already.

"What do you want me to do?"

"Please help us. We are really very confused and have to take a step that can change our lives forever. My uncle has spoken so much about you. Please help us out!"

Rudra looked at the young man standing in front of him. He appeared to be a man involved in business. He was in his early twenties but had already seen much of life and wealth. He had that sombre and aristocratic look about him. The girl was not more than five feet tall but she had an earthy beauty about her that overshadowed her obvious poverty. She had beautiful eyes that seemed to be always on the verge of tears. She was not more than twenty years old. Rudra stared at the couple and a strange sadness seeped into his very being. He realized that his breathing had once again become very calm and controlled. He was certain that something was going to force him to speak and look into the future of this young couple. He asked them to follow him into the cottage and he entered the bedroom and sat down on Baba's prayer mat. He really had no option. All this was beyond him. Somebody was pulling the strings and he was merely responding to the invisible tug.

He stood up, entered the bathroom and washed his hands, feet and face. He returned and wore a bandana over his head. Something propelled him to light a few incense sticks. He sat down, shut his eyes and began to flow with the moment. All the while he chanted his Master's name. Then it happened once again.

"Your mother is against this relationship…"

"Yes."

"Your father has no say in the matter. Though he is a good man with good intentions, he does not have the courage to stand up for you…"

"But he loves us a lot…"

"He does love you both a lot but he fears your mother more. It's sad but true. Not his fault. As a child he was made to appreciate survival more than selfless love. He was taught to hide rather than stand up for his belief and conviction. As a child he was made to feel guilty about expressing joy and being happy thus now he hesitates to stand up for love and happiness. Anyway you are here because your family does not want you to get married to this child. They object due to religion, financial disparity and social standing."

"Yes…"

"No, my son. They actually object because they have proposals from other families who are willing to pay a lot of money in dowry, if you marry their daughter. Lots and lots of money, of which you have no idea…"

"But they keep telling me that money is not of importance. My mother…"

"Whoever tells you that money is of no importance is shadow boxing. The fact is that they do not want you to get married because this girl's family cannot pay the dowry that your family desires."

"But why should we want dowry? We are extremely rich..."

"Your cousin brother got married recently..."

"Yes!"

"He got as dowry, apart from lots of money and ornaments and other things, a very big house abroad..."

"My God, how do you know all this... Yes, he got a studio apartment in London, on Mayfair..."

"Your mother wants to compete with your father's sister... Your aunt who she does not get along with at all..."

"Oh yes, she hates my aunt. Poor thing, my aunt is a good woman who..."

"Now you want to know when you should marry this girl? Well, for that you will have to do a few things..."

"Anything for her..."

"Good. First and foremost you shall pray for two hours a day for the next forty days..."

"What!"

Every step of our life there are choices. Every choice you make and the manner in which you make it and carry it out, decides your growth and journey towards light or your further slide into very soul-numbing darkness. It is never too late but every time we delay our growth, the soul weeps, knowing that it shall take that much longer for the spark to merge with the Flame

"Is this your 'anything for her'?"

"I mean...I mean...I don't pray for two minutes. Two hours is just too much."

"Why is it too much? If you pray for just ten minutes for every hour you are awake you shall pray for more than two hours everyday. Are you trying to tell me you cannot keep ten minutes of every hour for God?"

There was silence in the room. For Rudra, all that was transpiring in the room seemed too surreal to be given any importance at all. He would wake up soon, was his logic and consolation, to grapple with this strange reality.

"Tell me son, in order to achieve your dreams, is ten minutes of each hour, asking too much of you?

"Noooo! The way you put it, does not sound too taxing... But what do I pray?"

"Anything you want. You worship Swami Akalkoth Maharaj..."

"My God, how do you know all this..."

"It is my business to know son... I deal in the realm of the soul, my child. It is a very taxing profession. There are no second chances in my line of work. Only the fortunate and the blessed are allowed to associate with Us, but once they do, We never ever let go of the partnership. That is why you are here. You did not want to come here but something forced you to come here. That force was the result of a long- term relationship, spanning many lifetimes and evolutions. Well, that we can talk about later. Now we come back to you and what you can do so that you will always be by her side for eternity. First and foremost, you shall pray for two hours a day. You shall light oil lamps, morning, evening and night. You shall keep aside five per cent of all that you have earned last year for charity. You shall give that money with your own hands to somebody or some charity house that really needs it. All this in forty days, mind you. The last thing; all money that you have saved, in cash and kind, you shall give it to this girl. Nobody should know about this, but you have to do this in forty days time. If you do all this, I promise you, for eternity this girl shall be only yours."

The boy nodded. He looked at the girl, who blushed and Rudra found it hard to breathe. Tears welled up in his tired brown eyes and his throat felt chocked. In a second, he had seen the future and it was as Baba had predicted.

"You shall take this money and put it in her name in a fixed deposit, in some reputed bank. All this has to be done in forty days. Do you understand?"

"I will, that is not a problem... But you promise she will be mine then and my family will not create any problem..."

"It will be beyond your family to stop your union with her. This is my word. And you my child, you shall come after two and a half months. You have to; do you understand?"

"Y...es."

"Good. Now go. God be with you. Allah Malik. Sai Ram."

So my child who wants to die but hasn't yet figured out a way to live, what does your soul throb with; yourself or Godliness?

The young couple stood up, touched Rudra's feet (he no longer flinched), and left the room. Rudra stood up and walked towards Seth.

"Make sure he does his prayers, charity and puts all his money in the girl's name. It is very important. Important for him and the girl."

"Rudraji, all will beings well?"

Rudra stood up and exhaled. He felt tired. So very tired that he was certain somebody had sucked the marrow out of his bones. He had seen the future; seen it in a glance. He felt sick, cold and even frightened. He looked at Mr. Seth and saw deep concern and helplessness.

"The boy will die in nine weeks, Mr. Seth. I am sorry. There is nothing you or I can do about it. For his soul and for the future of this girl, Baba wants him to do all this. Prayers and charity will help his soul. The money will help this girl, who will never marry, thus will be able to look after herself till she dies at the age of forty-nine. She has nearly thirty years more of living to do. Baba wants her to be taken care of. If she suffers, then this boy's soul will never be at peace and trust me you don't want that to happen to your worst enemy, leave aside somebody you love. Make sure all this happens and keep quiet. If you don't, I will never allow you to meet. Ever. Do you understand me?"

"Don't letting him die, please Rudraji, don't letting him die. He is like my son..."

"In his astrological chart he has a life till seventy-eight. What has not been mentioned in the chart is that for more than fifty-years he will spend it on bed, paralyzed and with serious health problems resulting from the accident, he is going to be involved in nine weeks time. I would rather he dies once, than die everyday for the rest of his long life. Left to his destiny he would suffer for fifty or more years. He will not be able to deal with being called a cripple and he will not be able to deal with vegetating for half a century. You need lots of wisdom, strength, compassion and humour to be able to deal with tragedy. He does not have it. What he does have is His Master's grace. His Master, Swami Akalkoth Maharaj's blessings shall manipulate destiny and release this boy from years and years of humiliation and suffering. That is one of the reasons he has been asked to pray, do charity and settle this girl and her family. Their blessings and the blessings of those he shall give charity to and the power of the prayers and his Master's presence will save him from his own destiny. Now go and do as I have told, for not only will you secure this poor girl but will save a young man's very soul itself."

Mr. Seth touched Rudra's feet and Rudra realized that in reality Mr. Seth touched not his feet but the feet of his Master, Sai Baba of Shirdi.

But remember, whenever you pray, the most important thing to ask for is, strength and wisdom, love and compassion to accept whatever God/Master/Destiny has in store with grace and happiness and positive surrender. This is a must. This is mandatory. Without praying this, the life force of the prayer is virtually non-existent.

FOR AN HOUR or more Rudra just lay on the veranda sofa with his breathing gone haywire. He stared at the sea and after a while shut his eyes. The sadness still pervaded every cell in his body and his heart felt heavy. He wondered if what had transpired in there, with Seth and the young couple had anything to do with this lifeless and comatose state.

What was happening to him? And from where were all these strange predictions surging out? They obviously were coming from a source that had its astral fingers on the pulse of every living organism. How else could he have spoken with such authority about the young man's mother, father, grandmother and also pinpointed the young man's imminent death?

Rudra removed a cigarette and with great difficulty managed to light it, as the wind moved about with its usual exuberance. It began to drizzle and Rudra lay on his back, with a cigarette between his lips and stared at the wet world outside.

Where was the old man? He missed him. Rudra needed to talk to Baba and find out what the deuce was happening. The pain in his head was slightly better. He could open his mouth without feeling a dagger jab his temples.

He wondered what his kids were doing right now? It was nearing five-thirty. Would they still be at school or

---

Pray to your Master to fill your body, mind and soul; aura, vibrations, channel; every drop of blood, DNA and cell; with your Master's guidance, protection and presence. Pray to your Master to forgive you, lead you, guide you, guard you.

would they be at home? Were they doing well? Hope they weren't falling ill. When they cried did they miss him? When they saw the moon, they did remember him? Did they realize that he was dying without them? Would he ever hold them? Would he ever breathe freely and happily?

Rudra inhaled deeply and got up from the sofa. He went to the cabinet, picked up the bottle of Scotch and a glass, poured himself a large helping and slugged it down. The liquid felt like molten lava flowing down a mountain, scorching everything that came into its fiery path. The heat was so excruciating that he had no other option but to open his mouth, to suck in cold air. He poured himself another large peg, opened the freezer, grabbed a few cubes of ice, thrust them into the glass and walked back to the drawing room. The sun had set and darkness was setting in rapidly. Within him the sun had set long time and there was only darkness. Not nightfall but just death-like darkness.

Rudra switched on a few lamps and sat on the floor with his back to the wall and looked at the sea, heard the waves and noticed the winged species outside, preparing for the night.

Rudra shut his eyes and inhaled in deep. He did not want to cry. Let the world plot and allege against him, he would only love them and empathize. How could loved ones all of a sudden begin to hate? When you love truly, there is no place for hate. If hate still manages to crawl into the orbit, it only means there was a void in the heart that love hadn't filled, in order for hate, to manage a space for itself. That would mean your love wasn't all-encompassing. For if you truly loved somebody, you could never hate that person, no matter what that person did to you. Likewise Rudra could never hate those who were now against him; alleging nonsense; plotting; gossip mongering; influencing his own kids against him; turning turtle and switching sides, knowing he was all alone while the band of hypocrites got larger by the hour.

Rudra raised his glass to the sky and the sea and the world at large. He raised a toast to his kids who he longed so much that even death would no longer be a release from the pain he felt at their absence. He raised a toast to Baba who, he knew, saw all and understood and forgave and never, ever, judged.

Rudra slowly began to sip his drink. The night was young. The bottle was still full bodied. He had a long way to go.

THREE DAYS LATER, Rudra returned to the cottage and could smell the sweet fragrance of Baba's *chillum*. He rushed to the veranda and hugged Baba's feet. The old man sat at his usual place on the sofa. That section of the sofa was reserved for Baba. Rudra never sat on that revered space.

For a minute or more Rudra put his forehead on Baba's feet while the old man gently caressed Rudra's long unkempt hair.

"Except for one night where you drank nearly half the bottle of liquor, you seemed to have really followed the path."

Rudra smiled and both the men began to chuckle. Nothing was secret between them. Rudra was certain,

Baba was aware of his every thought, word and deed.

"I had to break the bottle in the end to make sure you stopped drinking."

Rudra nodded. He had carried the bottle to the veranda and it had slipped from his grasp and fallen off the balcony and onto the parapet where it had broken into many pieces.

"Don't leave me and go Baba. I can't handle life without you."

"My child, I am with you constantly. Whenever you think of me I am with you. If you want your Master to be with you all the time then you must think and miss your Master all the time. Take His or Her name all the time. The law is simple: If you want your Master with you, then you too must be with your Master and I guarantee you that your Master will be with you. As you sow thus you shall reap my son. So, your friend, Seth has begun to spread your name to his circle of friends and family?"

"Baba what is happening? I mean all this is serious stuff. Somebody can get hurt with all this prediction business. Take that boy for instance. Because of me, the boy shall sell off all his shares and stocks and give the money to that young girl of his. He has been asked to do charity and prayers. All this because I was made to

First and foremost go back into your flame and pray to Her to cleanse your body, mind and soul; aura, vibrations and channels; every drop of blood, DNA and cell, from all negativity and ill health. Thank the flame for protecting you, guiding you and guarding you.

understand, and don't ask me by whom, that the boy is going to die soon and thus all these steps are necessary for his soul and karmic balance sheet. But Baba, what if all this is not true? I mean, you understand, the consequences if all this is not true…"

"Are you calling me a liar, son?"

"Baba, for God sake, of course not. You are everything to me. Your word is my command. You and only you matter to me. You are all wise and knowing. You are omnipresent and omnipotent, for I know that you and God have merged and there is no difference between the two of you. Just like there is no difference between that sea and the waves. The sea is a part of the waves and the waves are a part of the sea. They are one and the same; it's just the form that differs. I know that. But Baba I am a loser. I have ruined my life and because of me, in a way I have ruined the lives of my children. I can't think straight to help myself thus how can I help others in need?"

"You are like the world's best surgeon who can perform the most complicated operations on others but can't give himself a simple injection. That doesn't mean the surgeon is a loser. That doesn't mean he knows nothing about surgery. He can't perform on himself and that's the way it is. You are a dervish. You are a medium. You are a channel. No matter what the world or those against you think or opine, don't you ever doubt yourself. Karmas and karmic linkages are too elaborate and entwined. You have lived for many lifetimes and you have lived it with many of whom you are associated with; be it family ties or friends or even those who don't get along with you or try to harm you emotionally, physically and spiritually. All belong to a soul group. You all have travelled together for lifetimes. You have all shared various relationships with each other. Father, mother, husband, wife, grandparents, uncle and aunt, son, brother, sister, cousins, in-laws, friend, servant, neighbours, driver and even many a times so-called enemies. Each person belonging to the soul group tries to help the other move spiritually and reduce the karmic baggage. Sometimes the soul who loves you the most, might willingly take birth as an enemy or a tormentor in a lifetime, just to help you work out your karma. Thus imagine, a person who you think hates you or wants to finish you off and in return you hate, might be you're your greatest well-wisher spiritually. He or she may be responsible for your turning spiritual or compassionate. That very person who is creating hell in your life may bring you closer to God and prayers and spirituality but is doing so in a manner that hurts you in the present lifetime, but maybe, that is the only way you will learn the lesson. Sometimes a soul is reborn just to comfort you and be there like a rock of strength to you, because you will need that support and strength. So son, tell me, who is your friend and who is your enemy? Maybe they all are your soul-family wanting to help you and you helping them in turn. Sometimes an opportunity comes in the form of a disaster. Sometimes

Destiny is a road map that points out the general direction, major destinations and gives an overview of the journey to be undertaken. Avoiding potholes, bad roads and speed breakers and using common sense are at the discretion of the driver.

the only way God can find place in your heart and life is through pain and sorrow and turmoil. Life is strange my son and thus never form judgments or abuse or hate or say nasty things about people. Who knows, you may be harming the one who loves you the most spiritually. Son, life is not that simple. Son we all are entwined in karma and in God. Don't hurt or hate or abuse anybody as you don't know, you may be hurting your dearest and most beloved, but you can't recognize it as the soul is wearing a different body in this particular lifetime. But always remember, I am there for you and I am there with you and let me see who harms a hair on your head my boy. But if I feel, it is best for your soul and your spiritual growth and karmic cleansing that you go through accidents, disasters, emotional and physical turmoil and tragedies, then so be it, as I am your Master and I know what is best for your larger good; I know what is best for your overall good; physical, emotional, material, intellectual and most important of all, best for your spiritual good. The Guru is all knowing my son and the Guru knows what is best for His or Her child. The Guru knows at what speed the child has to travel and how heavy the cross should be and how fast the karmic cleansing should be. Leave it all to your Guru. The Guru knows best and knows it all. You have all your life wanted to serve. Well, your most fervent desire has been fulfilled. Whatsoever you most fervently want shall be granted; either in this lifetime or you will have to come again to experience what you have so fervently desired. That is the rule of nature. It never deprives its child of anything. How you go about using that gift nature has bestowed on you, is up to each individual.

You have wanted to serve mankind and now you are being prepared to serve mankind. Not just those living but even those in the spirit world. If you doubt or resist, the process will only be more difficult. If you flow with nature, you shall swim the stormiest oceans with a smile."

"Baba I doubt all this happening. Why me? I am not religious? I drink, smoke and indulge in everything that is looked down upon by most religions. Why would I be chosen for such heavy duty spiritual work?"

"Son, right and wrong is a state of mind. The world hangs a man who has killed another human being and gives a medal to a soldier who has killed hundreds of human beings. It's all a state of mind, my child. The intention of the soul is more important than all the earthly laws put together. Now get me some of your ghastly tea and we will discuss how to be a good medium and help mankind through channeling."

Rudra smiled, kissed Baba's hand and both men chuckled once again. It was so good to have Baba next to him that Rudra couldn't help but cry.

"EVERY LIVING ORGANISM can be used as a channel, a medium, an instrument, for the Masters and the spirit

You are a medium. Always remember this. You are not the doer but the channel through which energy and the breath of God flows. For a moment do not entertain any illusion that you have power or are spiritually on a higher plane.

world, to work through. Zarathustra, the Holy One, who is considered the oldest known prophet or the first sage, who gave the world the philosophy, that there is only one God and that God is omnipresent, omnipotent, all-knowing and all wise and compassionate and this God, whom he called Ahura Mazda, had no form or colour. Zarathustra, the Holy One, was the first known medium or channel or instrument of the Lord. He was the first one to empty his body and allow the spirit of God to enter and speak through Him. The Zoroastrians, which also comprise of Parsees and Iranis, pray to Ahura Mazda and their prayers are written down in their Holy Book called the Avesta. Zarathustra meditated and channeled God and His commune is found in the Holy Ghathas; known as the Songs of Zarathustra.

"My son, if you read any Holy Scripture, belonging to any ancient religion, you will realize that the teachings, the wisdom, the way the words have been framed and the philosophy and the hidden esoteric meaning and compassion and love that flow through the pages cannot have been penned or thought or formulated by a human being. Take any Holy Book belonging to any ancient religion and you will be overwhelmed by the depth and wisdom that is crystal clear and very often, the more you dwell onto the meaning of the apparently simple words, you realize that there are deeper meanings and more pathways to the same sentence. The *Ramayana*, the book that contains the life of Lord Rama and His philosophy was written by Valmiki. And who was Valmiki? He was a dacoit who one day realized and embraced the God within him and turned into a sage. Now do you think it is this reformed dacoit who really wrote the *Ramayana* or was he used as a channel for the Holy Spirit to enter and pen the script. Prophet Mohammed was known to neither write nor read. Have you read the Holy Quran? It is sublime. It preaches peace and is a vast outpouring of gratitude to the Maker. All the Sages and Prophets allowed themselves to be used as vessels to carry the Word of the Lord to the people for thousands of generations. Of course, the vessel has to be strong to be able to carry the weight of the Holy Word; the vessel has to be empty of all that is not pure; the vessel has to be clean to preserve the sanctity of the Holy Word. Every Holy Book preaches one to pray and meditate; preaches one to be content and at peace with the plans of the Maker. Why? Because when you pray and meditate and are at peace and content with your Lord and Master, then you allow yourself to become a vessel; a medium; an instrument for the Holy Spirit to enter you. Through you, the Holy Spirit touches the lives of innumerable people; through you, the Holy Spirit guides and predicts; through you, the Holy Spirit helps, not only those on the physical plane but also those in the spirit plane. Son channeling is as old as creation. You must have read in most Holy Books, how animals and birds and fish have come to the rescue of noble ones. Those times, the Holy Spirit has used them, the animals and birds and fish, as vessels to carry out the Holy work. The stronger and cleaner and purer the individual, the more powerful and clear, he or she becomes, as a vessel or an instrument, to carry the Holy Word and be filled with the Holy Spirit. It is the birthright of every living organism, to become the medium and vessel, for the Lord above. We all are instruments; but instruments and vessels of what, is something that is left to the discretion of each individual. Do you want to be the medium for the Holy Word or do you want to be the instrument to spread hate and evil? Do you want to be filled up with your petty self and petty wants and needs or do you want to empty yourself of all but the spirit of God? It is not difficult. It all depends on what you really want. Do you want God or yourself to satisfy your needs? If you want God to be within you; if you want to be a dervish or a medium or a channel, then you need to let go of yourself and embrace God within you. Actually, you don't even have to embrace God within you. If you empty yourself of all those thoughts and desires and greed and hate and obsessions, automatically the Spirit of the Lord enters you. Remember, in you, only one can reside: you or your Master. There is no place for two to rule. And anybody and everybody can be a medium or a vessel for God's work. The more you fill yourself up with your Master's name and thought, the more you get filled up with His or Her energy and automatically you become a medium for your Master."

"You mean once you become a medium you begin to have psychic powers?"

"Son, there are types of mediums. Many types. You might become a very noble human being who will be ready to help and serve mankind, through any given means. You might become a medium of charity. You might become a medium to fight for the weak. You might become a vessel for organizing aid for those who desperately need it. The Holy Spirit might use you to develop a medicine that will benefit millions of people.

You might be used to fight cases free of cost for those innocent but too poor to afford an excellent lawyer. You might, all of a sudden, begin to feed the poor or serve animals. You might compose music, or write a book, or direct a movie that will inspire people to become better or wiser and more compassionate human beings. Son, you might be used to simply become a better persona and inspire all those who come in contact with you to become better human beings. Yes, you might be used as a healer; a psychic medium; a champion for the disabled; a warrior for the damned; oh my son, your life will be no longer yours, so you might be used for a particular cause or for all these things at one time. Let your Master decide what the vessel should carry; let your Master decide what tune the instrument should play; let your Master fill you up with whatever rhythm you should dance to. Well, we have decided that you shall be used to guide people in working out their karma. So be it. Now get me my *chillum*. This vessel needs to smoke."

Rudra sat by Baba's feet and pressed the old man's ankles. He still couldn't accept the fact that Heaven was so short staffed that it needed a loser like him to be their vessel for all this karmic jazz.

"Let Him decide which instrument is well tuned to compose which tune, my son, and also let Him decide who is a loser and who a winner. Now get my *chillum* and let's fill our vessel with sweet smoke."

Rudra began to chuckle. The old man was impossible.

Work and live to annihilate your little petty ego and bask in the glory and presence of your Master, God and Goddess.

BABA WANTED TO have just soup for dinner. Rudra went to the market and shopped for the ingredients. He used to love making different types of soups for his children. He would make a huge bowl, enough for three families. His daughter would often tease him that he resembled a witch doctor, while preparing the soup; for the simple reason that he would stand with a huge ladle and continue to stir the soup for more than half an hour. He did resemble a tribal chief stirring a huge pot that comprised of all the vague ingredients, for the benefit of his clan.

His kids usually hated the soup.

Drinking the soup was mandatory.

Often even Rudra wanted to chuck the soup down his sink.

When no one looking, he did just that.

But the fact remained that the ghastly soup was very healthy.

Rudra returned home, drenched to the bone. The rain had waited for just the right moment, before it hurled itself on to him. He was on a stretch of road where there was no place to seek shelter, no cab or three-wheeler to stop and duck into. The darn stretch was half a mile long.

Rudra loved the walk though. He inhaled deep and took in the aroma of the earth and the fragrance of the flowers that grew wild on the open space of land. Beyond the land, he could see the wide sea and the coconut trees that swayed and danced to the wet rhythm of the pouring rain. When he was small he loved playing football in the rain, on top of a mountain plateau, with clouds floating low and the valley down deep below with its small farms that resembled chocolate pieces and villages that appeared to a cluster of small toy houses. Very often the gang would sit on the mountaintop and watch a bus traverse through the horizon and halt at innumerable spots. The bus was just a dot; an ant that moved and halted and often never moved for a long time.

Now as though in a blink of an eye he was already a middle-aged man, about to die anytime soon.

He wondered how in hell did the years and life itself zoom so fast, past him? Deep within him, Rudra felt he was still just a kid who loved to play and enjoy life and laugh and raise Cain and have a great time doing all this. He could still remember his first day at the boarding school. He got down from the bus, entered the dormitory and in seconds was surprised to be involved in a fist fight with an absolute stranger, who for the next ten years would be a close friend and a very hard working boy, who when just twenty, would die in a road accident. Where did all his other friends go? Were they all right? Did they think of him: the wild one? Were they doing well, emotionally, mentally, financially, and most of all, spiritually? He hoped all of them were healthy and

Usually, we hear the individual saying 'God is great, I was saved or not one member of my family came to harm'. Would God not be great if the individual or a family member would have come to harm? I've heard people saying my Master's hand was on my head thus nothing happened to me. Does that mean those who were injured did not have their Masters' hand and blessings on their head?

happy. He really did. Those were innocent times. The games that were his very life, be it cricket, football, even playing marbles at which he really sucked; the climbing of trees to pluck fruit or just explore new highs; the constant hunger pangs that compelled him and the gang to traverse through semi-forest to have a hot and edible dinner at one of the local restaurants in the market, that was out of bounds for him and his boarding school mates; the thrashing they got, if and when caught but that was all right...at least they were thrashed with a belly full of hot tasty dal and egg-curry and mutton biryani; playing games on mountain tops with the rains lashing and clouds making visibility not only doubtful but even dangerous but the games went on while they shivered and their bones felt numb and their teeth clattered; the gypsies with their small dirty but incredibly cute children and the buffaloes and donkeys that inevitably trailed behind the caravan; the cheating during examinations where Rudra had been blessed by the Gods above with a flair for the amoral bordering on the genius; missing home and aching for loved ones. Those were the days; life was horrible-beautiful-sad-joyful all rolled into one; one high that roller coasted into another.

"Son, this is positively the worst soup made in the history of mankind." Saying the obvious, Baba had the soup as though it was the most delicious nectar from the very heavens itself.

"Taste, too, is just a taste of mind. It all depends upon one's mood, the ambiance and manner in which it is served, with the folks you share the table, your health, your hunger pangs etc., etc., etc. One should just thank the Lord and eat what is kept in front of you and keep your opinions to yourself. If you are asked about your opinion then in the manner that would hurt the least, give your opinion. You cannot digest very oily or rich food and often you have remained hungry but not touched those dishes that you thought wouldn't agree with you. But by refusing to even touch the food, you have hurt those who have laboured many hours to bring those dishes in front of you. That is not correct. Take a little, just in honour of the love that has been poured into those dishes. Explain the reason why you are eschewing large helpings or certain dishes but do it with love and tenderness. So, if given the option, you avoid such food that one's metabolism rebels against. But if you have no option than to partake of such food, then take little of it and eat it very slowly. Don't hurt those who cook for you with love."

Rudra nodded.

"You know son, it takes talent to make such ghastly soup. Give me more of it please." Saying this, the old man smiled and Rudra, like a child, beamed with happiness.

Your faith should be such that even your Master gets shaken up but my child to shake your Master up, you should be ready to have the very foundations beneath you and the sky above you to be shaken up and your body, mind and soul and the world around you to be traumatized.

"YOU ARE WONDERING what is happening to you? How, all of a sudden, you have begun to predict things and see into the future? What is going on, you wonder? Are you really becoming a dervish or a medium or is all this, just some subconscious play taking place? Worst of all, you have begun to doubt your credibility and integrity, by assuming, you are fooling people by playing on their gullibility? But the fact of the matter remains, that neither your subconscious mind or your intelligence or your heightened sense of perception and reception where vibration is concerned, could have allowed you to be so accurate and see so clearly into the future. You know this but are unwilling to accept the truth, as the truth goes against all that which you have been taught, by a society that is constipated with superstitious beliefs and narrow-minded self-centeredness.

"Son, the Great Fakir, who the world calls Ahura-Ram-God-Allah-Durga, sees first and foremost intentions and then efforts. Success, is very karmic my child. It has nothing to with ability, intelligence or performance. You may be the finest actor or sports-person, but you need the break; you need the platform; you need the backing; you need the publicity and most important of all, you need to have success in your karmic blueprint. It all boils down to that. But God does not see all this. He sees your intentions, your love, your sacrifice and your efforts. Remember, eventually you will be granted success. In this life or another, success will be yours. The important thing is the intention. Why does a doctor keep awake day and night watching over a patient? Is it professional duty? Is it because of the burning need to fight illness? Is it money? Is it because of personal ego to always have a cent percent success rate? Is it for the fear of failure? Is it to serve and treat each patient as family? Is it to impress one's colleagues? Is it because the doctor cannot see anybody in pain and distress? Is it an amalgam of all or most of the above mentioned points? Or is there unhappiness at home, so the doctor would rather stay at the clinic or the hospital and keep busy and away from conflict and depression? Rudra, my son, the Great Fakir, sees first and foremost the intentions. Remember, for whatever reason the doctor is committed, as long as he is treating the patient, duty is being performed. That is first and foremost a very important point. It is better to have a responsible doctor take care of a patient solely for money, than a doctor be negligent about the patient and cause harm

Those who serve their Masters are served a million times more by their Masters. You serve first and foremost by being a decent human being. You serve by not harming others and by not gossiping and plotting and trying to create sadness and an environment of hate and pain. You serve by not alleging and trying to break families. Yes, you also serve by being a medium; by doing social work; by being generous; by lending a helping hand; by reaching out to the unfortunate or the unprivileged, by praying for peace and health for those who are in need for peace and health; for meditating for world peace; for feeding the hungry and clothing those in need and providing shelter to the homeless. There are a million ways to serve God, Goddess and your Master but always remember your Master sees and appreciates and serves you back a million times more.

or even be responsible for death. There is nothing wrong in the pursuit of money if that pursuit can be for the larger good. Also, if the doctor was to keep aside some percentage of his earnings for charity, the pursuit of money has a larger good and the fact that the more one earns, the more one gives, it is then wonderful, this pursuit for money as this pursuit contributes to the cycle of nature.

"The point is intentions and efforts are most important. Ensuing results come way behind where the Lord is concerned. We are concerned about your intentions. You have always wanted to serve. Always and thus after weighing your strengths and weaknesses and your state of mind, we decided that the best way for you to serve would be to be a medium to the Higher Forces; that you be involved in spreading light. The important thing is how best to walk the chosen path, be safe on the journey and most importantly, move closer to the source of light. Whether you are a medium, an artist, a plumber, a school- teacher, a prostitute, is of little importance."

"A prostitute?"

"Yes, a prostitute, too, is a human being. She has her own karma and often she has her own compulsions to be in the trade. Most women in our country take up this profession either due to poverty or some compulsion or the other. Either to support the family or they have been forced into the trade and now cannot get out, even if they want. That does not mean they are not the children of God. As long as a human being tries to walk the path of God; as long as a person wants to walk the path of light; that person is all right; as that person, just with intentions is already on the path. Who are we to judge? Let only the Fakir do the judging. Karma and destiny are very hard taskmasters. Whether a doctor, a yogi or a prostitute, the Lord sees first and foremost the intentions and the effort to walk the path of Light; all else comes later. If a woman, to support her family, indulges in prostitution, how is she any less moral than another individual? Yes, if the profession is indulged in for reasons like easy money, lust, power...then, matters take a different turn. But if the woman has no option and yet continues to work in her profession and support her family and be a decent human being, do you think the heaven above is going to denounce and abandon her? No! Never! But prostitution is of the soul. Be it a prostitute, a politician, a teacher, a housewife, whatever, if a person compromises his or her soul, then that is prostitution. The flesh matters little. It matters very little. The soul is of utmost importance. That is why, whether you are a medium or a prostitute, intentions and efforts to walk the right path, the path of light is of foremost importance. Whatever your profession, if your heart is clear and your thoughts noble, it doesn't matter why you are doing, whatever you are involved in, as long as

You want to give a gift to your Master then give your Master your very soul and you know what is the essence of the soul...it is faith. Faith is the heartbeat that keeps the soul pure and intact in its original glory despite having been put through lifetimes of depravity and darkness. Faith keeps God from pulling the plug off from creation. Love and faith are two sides of eternity.

you are trying to be a decent human being; not hurting the innocent, trying your best to walk the path of light. A person, who may be known as a man or woman of God; may be eschewing all pleasures of the flesh; but could be doing it to impress the world or show how noble and pious, he or she is or could be, all day, dreaming ways and means of satisfying body urges; such a person doesn't come too high on our list of light workers. My child, a person's intentions, love and effort, are of utmost importance to God and also is the best nourishment for the soul. Yes, there are people, who are driven mad by ignoble thoughts; they do not want to think such thoughts but are too weak or too caught up in them; but they want to walk the path of light and really try to walk the noble path and suffer truly and painfully, when they stray; son, these children of the Lord, are too on the path of light. Heaven judges them tenderly, for their intentions and efforts are noble and they are working on their weakness. Son, that is why, never ever judge anybody; don't indulge in slander; don't criticize; don't get into verbal arguments; don't condescend. Just walk the path, quietly, humbly and in total positive surrender. Now, let's talk about you and your life as a medium."

"THERE ARE A few things one must never forget on one's journey as a medium. Most important, you are the instrument, a vessel, wherein divine light and energy flows into and flows through. All the miracles that take place through the medium are because of the Master and the divine plan. The medium or channel is just what these words denote; an instrument or a vessel. Whether you are a medium for healing or predictions, the medium should never forget that he or she is not the doer but just the channel through which the healing or prediction are taking place. Of course, for perfect clarity and purity in healing and predictions, the medium should be in perfect sync with the Master and the Master's energy. The flute should be clean and none of its seven holes should be blocked but should be in perfect shape, vibration, colour, speed and depth, for the breath of the Master to flow through and divine music to flow out. Thus, it is very important, in fact it is crucial that the medium is always empty of everything but the breath of God; the medium is filled only with the Master's energy; the mind is empty of the ego but throbbing with the divine name. It is when these conditions exist, that divine music flows through, uninterrupted, clear and in perfect melody. You are like the piano. Divine energy is the music; the Master, the greatest Musician. Not for a moment should the piano take the credit for the phenomenal music that is created and which flows through it, for it is the Musician that is responsible for the melody. There are thousands of pianos but only one

Just help people. That is the best way you can thank God for all that God has done for you and your family. For all that which God has bestowed on you and your family, help those in need. You want to show your gratitude to God then help those in need. Just give and give and give and help those in need.

Musician. But yes, the piano must be in tune. The instrument must be in shape, with all chords intact; neither too loose nor too rigid and tight; for if the piano is not in perfect shape, the divine melody will never come through the way it is supposed to; for the simple reason; the piano is flawed. So my son, it is imperative and mandatory that the medium should be devoid of the self but satiated with divine energy."

"But Baba how can one be filled with divine energy all the time? Also Baba, one is not channeling every moment of the day, thus why is there a need to be devoid of the self all the time?"

"My son, let us first discuss the ways of being filled with divine energy all the time. You know my boy, you, who make the worst tea and soup in the universe, are already filled with divine energy most of the day."

"No, I'm not. Most of the time I'm hurting within…"

"Whoever told you, that if you are filled with divine energy, you cease to feel pain of body, heart and mind? Every prophet and child of God has gone through more mental-physical-spiritual anguish than the common man. They have wrestled with dilemmas of the soul and been anguished over the plight of mankind. They have been ridiculed and tormented and they have had their doubts and their moments of darkness and depression. All the while filled with divine energy. What is the meaning of being filled with divine energy? Do you think, it is something out of Universal Studios, where the sky will open and celestial beings will shower your thick head with fragrant flowers or angels will swoon down and play the harp for you? My boy, being filled with divine energy means, being connected to the Live Wire, through which flows the Life Force; which has all the answers and all the questions; which helps you to dispel darkness and bring light to those who really need it. Being filled with divine energy means being released by your ego and being free of your own self.

"As I told you before, in your soul, there is place for only one being; there is place for only one alphabet; I or U! Your soul can only accommodate one. I: stands for the individual ego; that is trapped with conflicting desires, self-centered needs and petty inhibitions and grandiose deceits. U: stands for God. U stands for Thou. So my child who wants to die but hasn't yet figured out a way to live, what does your soul throb with; yourself or Godliness. You, my boy, hurt and ache for the loss of your children; the anguish of being maligned; the desperation of being hunted and ruined; the lack of freedom to exhale in peace. But my son, if I were to cut my own arm now, it is going to hurt and it is going to bleed. However spiritually up there I may be, howsoever filled with divine energy, if I let the rules of mother earth play their course, then I am going to hurt and bleed. Yes, if I manipulate the rules or if I use divine powers,

Nobody is a victim. There are no preys and no hunters. Fill yourself up with God and selfless love and you shall be the shadow of God. Fill yourself up more with the Creator and after a while you will merge in God. Fill yourself further with the Maker and a time shall come when you too shall become God, as there shall be no difference between you and your Maker. Like the waves in the ocean; you too shall become the ocean.

then I shall not hurt, not bleed and have twenty-five books and movies made on the incident; which is pure manipulation of energy and vibrations and has nothing to do with spirituality. There is no magic in fish swimming in the water and birds flying and human beings conversing and discriminating. They are simply following certain laws of the earth. So, my boy you do hurt and yet, you are filled with divine energy, for your mind, when not absorbed in the moment, is free of the self. When you are not in the moment, you are taking Sai Baba's name. You are taking Meher Baba's name. You are chanting a mantra. You are looking at the flame and thinking of me. You are praying to Devi. You chant Islamic prayers. You don't think and plan and hate and want to get back in a violent or negative manner at your detractors. You don't wish anybody harm. You have never tried to hurt or harm anybody. You have not planned to disturb people or spread rumours about them. You are in your world of music, books, TV, cigarettes and alcohol and with God. You talk and behave with respect. You don't look down upon anybody. You try and help those in need of it. You are filled with divine energy through the day. The more you chant your Master's name, the more you spend time in meditation and prayer, the more you soak yourself with the divine spirit, the more clear and clean and well-tuned a medium you shall be. The more receptive a medium you shall be. You shall allow your Masters to be able to channel you in more ways and for longer periods. Through the day and yes, even when you sleep, you will be used as a medium to help and spread the light. All you have to do is be in the moment and be with your God and Master.

Do one thing at a time and give it your best. Don't judge and don't seek fruits. Don't expect anything. Just be in total and positive surrender to the will of God. Pray that you receive wisdom and strength, love and compassion, to accept with total positive surrender and grace, all that your Master and your destiny have in store for you. Remember, you must accept your fate and your Master's wishes, with positive surrender and grace. Most people accept their lot but with anger and resignation and frustration. That beats the whole purpose of the experience. Know that your Master has planned everything for you, so that you grow and you give and you receive and you get cleansed, with grace and with total positive embrace of your Master's will. Aware that your Master will do only what is best for you and your loved ones. Now get me that ghastly tea."

Rudra, for a long time, kept massaging Baba's feet. Then he inhaled deep and sighed. He must have done something really good in one of his miserable past lives, to have been graced with Baba's presence.

But if a person was consumed with anger and rage then after death, the mental, emotional and spiritual angst and anger and negativity would still be carried over. The person will have to make an effort to let go of the negativity. If he or she doesn't, then the soul can be earth-bound. The person would be neither at peace in the spiritual plane nor at peace on earth. An extremely unpleasant situation to be in and till the anger and negativity is not converted to love and compassion, the soul remains in limbo. By limbo, we mean a state of stagnation and rot.

"Yes, you have. You served me. For lifetimes you have served me and I have protected you and guided you and made sure you advance but have failed to teach you how to make good tea."

Both the men laughed aloud and Rudra hugged Baba close and the old man kissed the sobbing young one and ruffled his unkempt long hair.

THEY WERE ON the beach. It was still very early in the morning. The sun had made its presence felt for a while, then, as though it had a change of heart, it settled behind a mischievous group of clouds, pretending it had never bathed the little sea port with its luminous blessings.

Baba and Rudra were on the beach. They walked bare footed on the wet sand. All around, the trees, the sea and the very sky seemed as though painted with a dull shade of silver; as though a photographer had put a lens that made the world look dull silver.

The water gushed towards both the men as though to greet them with her wet embrace but by the time the exuberant wave could reach them, she could barely manage a soft caress.

Rudra had slept badly. Baba had hardly slept at all. The young man had tossed and turned and grappled and lost the fight with the demons of his subconscious mind, while Baba had sat and prayed. He prayed for the peace of the world; for the weak and the helpless; for those in pain and in illness; for the hungry and the abandoned; for the earth-bound souls who were clinging to earth in their ignorance or their lust for the material or the maddening pull of loved ones; he prayed for animals and birds who were tortured or lay in captivity; for lovers and for the jilted; for children and parents to surround each other with love and peace, whether they were living as a family or had decided, in their karmic blueprint, to go their separate ways. Baba prayed for all those who prayed to God and HIS army of Masters and Light workers. Baba prayed for Rudra. Not that his demons leave him but that he be filled with strength and wisdom, love and compassion and lots of humour to handle all that which was in store for him, with complete grace and positive surrender to God's will. For a long while, Baba observed Rudra sleep. The old man observed Rudra's aura and realized that there was a vast difference in the aura while he was awake and while he slept. During the day, Rudra's vibrations and aura ranged from blue to purple to shades of gold. Vibrations of an advanced light worker and seeker of God. During his sleep, though all the colours of the aura remained, there was a change. A combination of colours that showed severe hurt and pain; guilt and humiliation and soul crippling longing merged with his inherent aura and Baba saw the man in his true image; a man who was devastated by the loss of his children but who held no malice or hate towards those responsible for creating circumstances of separation and distance. He had no anger or hate in his aura. None whatsoever. He held himself as responsible as he held the mother of his

The greatest myth is that death puts an end to all suffering. Yes, death puts an end to all suffering related with the body and circumstances.

children accountable for the situation they were in. The guilt in the man was not about what had happened but about what was happening to his children. But the man had no malice in him.

Baba turned towards Rudra who walked with his head held high observing the hazy horizon. He loved this battered man who all his life had wished nobody harm and who still loved all those who had turned bitter and negative towards him. Baba sighed. He was aware that sometimes, to serve the poor and the needy and be able to paint a grander picture on a very sizeable canvas that would inspire and embrace humanity, one had to go through the shedding off of lifetimes of karma at a pace that left the soul breathless and wrenched from its very foundations. The cleansing was done so swiftly that it left the person whirling about, numb and dazed. When the dust settled, either you loved God or hated the Creator or just did not believe in His-Her existence. Either you became calm and steady with the realization that this was karmic cleansing, and it hurt like the dickens, but it was for the larger good; not only for *your* larger good but for the larger good of all or you became negative and cynical and felt betrayed and turned your back on God for having deserted you when you needed the Old Chap the most. Either it results in positive surrender and graceful acceptance or everything metamorphoses into anger, hate, self-pity and darkness. Both ways you hurt. The difference is the source of the spring from which the pain gushes through. That makes all the difference. Not only to one's state of mind but also to one's state of spirituality. For if you can accept the Lord's will with grace, then you move on to the next level. It only validates the belief that God gives each of us a cross to bear, knowing well that you have the capacity to lift it up and not be crushed by it. The good Lord knows what each of us is capable of carrying and if you get crushed under the cross then you've not only let yourself down and your spiritual and karmic growth get affected but you have also let God down by not living up to the faith the Creator reposed in you by allowing and entrusting you with the Cross.

"Every step of our life there are choices. Every choice you make and the manner in which you make it and carry it out, decides your growth and journey towards light or your further slide into very soul-numbing darkness. It is never too late but every time we delay our growth, the soul weeps, knowing that it shall take that much longer for the spark to merge with the Flame; the Flame of everlasting peace and happiness and most of all, everlasting bliss. The soul longs for that Eternal Flame; it longs for that Blissful Ocean and every step forward, takes the soul towards It and every step backwards takes the soul to the void of darkness and everlasting guilt, hate and perpetual conflict, of all negative emotions brewing at one time but for all eternity. The soul dreads that dark void where for all eternity the soul carries guilt, hate, anger, lust, greed, doubt and worst of all eternal unrest and frustration.

Now just because the person has left the physical body, it does not mean the emotions and the overpowering sense of rage are no longer felt. The mind doesn't cease to exist.

The soul dreads this darkness. It thus seeks to travel towards the Eternal Flame. It yearns to travel towards the Light. But the individual is so engrossed in petty games and immediate gratifications that it mistakes the false glitter for the Great Light. It mistakes the mirage for the Ocean. All the while, travelling at soul wrenching speed backwards towards darkness; towards eternal void.

Baba did not say a word but Rudra heard everything. He halted and faced the Old Man.

"You were talking to me and you explained everything without even moving your lips. How do you do all this Baba?"

"You and I swimming in the same current. We are connected to the same Live Wire. We are in the same moment. We are thus travelling the pace and we are going in the same direction. You are bound to hear what I think and say. I spoke to you through the vibrations that we have connected ourselves with. It comes only when you are in the present moment, calm and in positive surrender to the will of our Lord. So you heard it all clearly?"

"Yes Baba."

"That is the same way you hear me speak and then I speak through you as a medium. You connect with me and then I speak through you. Less of you, means more of Me. More of you, means less of me. If you want me to speak through you, then you should empty your mind, heart and body of yourself, and allow me to settle within you. The moment you do that, I begin to speak through you. That is how channeling works. You could hear me speak even though I did not open my mouth. The same way I speak to and through you even though I am not physically present. Why should distance matter to us who work with light and energy. You watch television and hear the radio. Can you see the television channel or the radio station? Do you see the man speaking on the radio? You can watch hundred channels on the television; news from all over the world, taking place that very moment. How do you see and hear all this? All this is possible through energy and vibrations and waves in the air that carry that message or channel or news, thousands of miles away, from continents far away and sometimes from another planet itself. The same way my dear son, who prepares ghastly tea that make me shudder and concocts soups that makes the very heavens weep, channeling is done through Masters and Their mediums. This is the same way in which inspiration comes through. What is inspiration? You are trying to solve a problem. You have done all your research and you have done all your analysis and yet the solution is no longer visible. It seems impossible. Then suddenly one fine day you are having a bath, relaxed and far away from your problems or you are sitting under an apple tree just seeing the clouds above and wham, your solution 'dawns' upon you. It hits you like lightening. It is so simple and yet so profound. You wonder why you haven't thought of it before? How come now all of a

Suicide is of no use. If you think you are miserable now, you have no idea how miserable you are going to be after your soul is forced to leave its body by the act of suicide.

sudden when least expected it has popped out of some recess of your subconscious mind? But son, the fact is, you have been guided by your Master or your spirit guide or your loved one who is no longer in the flesh but very much concerned for your well being, even though in the spirit world. But most importantly, you have allowed them to help you out by being open and receptive and keeping your mind like a blank sheet of paper on which they could scribble the solution to your problem. If your mind is like a paper that has not a syllable worth of space, how are They going to help out with the answer. They need your space, your time, your calm energy and your receptiveness, for your antenna to pick up the channel to broadcast what they want you to receive. First of all the TV should be in working condition, then the TV should be charged either with the right wires and connections or with the right batteries to fuel it. The waves are filled with information. All you need is the right equipment to receive it. A calm mind, that accepts with grace and surrender, all that which God has in store, is the perfect instrument.

"Being in the present moment means having the antenna to receive the information. Being in the state of meditation allows the antenna to probe, space travel, seek and get the information you desire. Your body and mind should be like the TV set that can first procure the programme and then be able to screen it with the right clarity and volume. This is how a medium works my son. You don't need to have people coming for predictions to be a medium. The moment you allow your Master to reside in you, you become a medium. You will be used to serve. Your presence will help those in need. Your touch will be a transmitter for your Master's touch. You inquired as to the need for being in constant commune with your Master and God through chanting His or Her name or being just in the present moment. Well, it's simple. The reason is you never know when you will be need to serve and help and be an instrument for your Master's energy. You may be having a meal and a friend in distress might call and confer with you on a problem that could destroy your friend's future; your friend needs guidance; don't you think if you are in the moment, the guidance will come through from your Master; rather than your own muddled and preconceived notions? You need to be in the moment and with your Master all the while, so that you can serve all the time. You need to be filled with the Divine energy so that whatever you are involved in; whatever profession; whatever occupation; your Master is working through you. Now let's turn back and eat some of those tasty biscuits you got yesterday. We shall dip them in the tea and pray to the Good Lord above to make sure that even the tea gets the taste of the biscuits and we can pretend to be having tasty biscuits with delicious tea."

Rudra bit his upper lip controlling his laughter. He nodded as though trying to say ' just you wait Old Man,

For the soul, all it takes is a pure thought and he or she will be with you. But by constantly grieving, you are chaining your son and your loved one. Don't! Its hell or should I say, its worse than hell. Hell is nothing but a state of mind. Why make your loved one go through such a state of mind, filled with grief, anger and helplessness?"

just you wait'. Then he began to laugh and he held the
Old Man's arm and both the men walked towards their
cottage that was still bathed in silver and the morning
dew.

IT WAS LATE at night. They ate a simple dinner of rice
and dal. There were a few bottles of pickles and chutneys
to choose from and Baba scooped out a little from this
bottle and a little from here, and his meal looked a
perfect hodge-podge of varying tastes and aromas. Baba
mixed all that was put on his plate and with a short
prayer he ate whatever was put before him. He never
inquired as to what was being cooked or from where
the food came or there was very less salt or too much of
this or none of that. Though Rudra tried his best to
cook every dish with love and make it as delicious as
food prepared by a contented and proficient cook, he
very often fell flat on his face. Not that the food was
unpalatable. It just didn't taste right. But not once did
Baba ever comment on the taste or the lack of it. Never
did he wince whilst chewing something that certainly
looked like spinach but definitely tasted like burnt
cucumber. He ate every morsel of every dish, that ranged
from mediocre to downright gruesome, with the same
grateful acceptance. Never had he joked, not even once,
about Rudra's absolutely disastrous culinary attempts.

Baba would first wash his hands and face. Then say
a short prayer of gratitude. Then, he would make sure
that Rudra's plate was stacked with all the best edible
pieces and then he would take a little of this and peck a
bit of that. He ate very little. He chewed slowly. Baba

even enjoyed Rudra's food; which was something that really mystified Rudra, for he failed to see any source of enjoyment to be had from consuming his miserable attempts with 'sauce and spice'.

It was a well-lit sky. The moon appeared to be satiated, with her own lusciousness; like a woman who was certain, she would burst due to the intense love and craving for her lover. The clouds hovered around the moon; just as, inevitably, beauty is always surrounded by admirers; not only surrounded but in fact, lured, like moths to a flame. Beauty may be skin deep, but damn it, the heart too resides under that very skin; and in that heart, reside brewing volcanoes, hurricanes that can sweep away in their very fury and passion everything that comes in their way and also scorching heat that can burn everything it even caresses and an ocean of intense and conflicting emotions that can drown the entire world. So don't tell me beauty is skin deep. Yeah it is and that is where the problems start, for God's sake.

"Most human love and all that which comes with it is a state of mind. Very often, it is a state of mind that the heart wants to be in. I love that blank look you get when you don't understand anything I am talking about but yet want to understand everything that is within me. Come let's take a walk on the beach. It won't rain for forty minutes anyway…"

"It never rains when you are taking a walk outside. Don't think I haven't observed. Even though the clouds

So, if you really love the person who has left the physical world, pray, give in charity and live gracefully.

seem to be bursting with water, they shall not open up and pour till you are safely back indoors. Don't think I don't observe, ok? Two days back it was raining as though the very heavens had got a plumbing problem and then you decide to go for a stroll and I saw you stand on the veranda and you looked at the sky and in twenty-four seconds the rain stopped. Stopped completely. Did not slow down or become a drizzle. The rains just stopped falling. And with a smile and a short prayer of gratitude, you coolly walked about and came back and then bang, somebody up there once again switched on the tap and it began to pour. So don't think I don't observe. Yeah, I might not understand half the things you say but I observe."

"You really are a funny man, my son, with a very wild imagination. You should begin writing books. God help us all, but you should. Ha! Ha! Now where was I?"

"You said something like, it is a state of mind that the heart wants to be in? Lord, love a defrosted duck, what on earth does that mean, Baba?"

"It means that very often, the heart wants to be in love and it convinces the mind that it is in love. The heart convinces every cell that it is in love and everything is going to be perfect. The very concept of being in love is so alluring that the mind too follows the dictates of

I have eaten every meal with you as you have always offered me the meal first, before putting a morsel in your mouth. I have seen all the fascinating sunrises and sunsets with you, as you asked me to be present with you, each time the sun did its illusionary dance."

the heart. The reason why I said that most human love is nothing but an altered state of mind is very simple. Two people fall in love. They spend hours and days and years together, in love. Then they have a problem and most often hate sets in. How can hate set in a heart for the same person, for whom only a short while back, this very heart beat for? Not only does hate enter but with hate, the desire to see that person suffer, never prosper, be humiliated and most of all, be miserable, also surface and vie for prominence. Let me tell you my son, in a heart that felt true love, there can be no scope for hate and ill will towards the loved one. It's not possible to burn the ocean. You can freeze it. You can have the water evaporate. But you can never burn the ocean. And whether you freeze it or evaporate it, the fact remains, the water still exists but in a different form. It never really ceases to exist. Defrosting or rainfall is just round the corner. In a heart that has truly loved, you might feel immense anger but hate and all her obnoxious sisters have no place. That is why, most often, love is a state of mind. Once you have true love, why just the heart and mind, all the forces of nature are yours to mould and nurture. They are yours to serve and be served; loved and be loved; to give and receive; to open and to embrace. True love, son, is an extension of God and wherever God is present, negative emotions have no place to brew their venomous poison."

They sat for a while on the sand. Rudra normally carried a rolled up bed-sheet, whenever Baba and he strolled on the beach. With the rains, often, the sand was wet and Rudra wanted Baba to be comfortable while he sat and observed the sea. Rudra spread out the sheet that had Donald Duck and Mickey Mouse printed onto a cream background. Both the men sat down on the sheet and observed the well-endowed moon, the fleeting clouds, the jubilant stars and the beckoning ocean.

NEXT MORNING, BABA and Rudra sat in their room, with the windows just slightly open, to let in cool breeze but to keep the rain water from splashing in. All through the night it had rained and it seemed there were many more hours of the downpour. They had just returned from the veranda, as the wind was cold and wet.

"Baba, you want some hot tea?"

"My Karmas are catching up with me so I guess I will go through the torture."

Sometime later, Rudra walked in with a tray that had two cups of tea and a plate of biscuits. In silence they sipped their tea and Rudra observed the flame that was constantly lit in their room. The room was partially dark and the intensity of the flame was felt all the more.

"It is a sad house, that doesn't have a flame burning, my son. If not for twenty-four hours, a candle or an oil lamp should be burnt at least twice a day; once in the morning and once at sunset or at night. That is the least one can do for one's family and one's soul. Fire is Creation. Fire is the physical manifestation of the Divine. It is what the Zoroastrians call 'the son of God'. Fire not only warms but most importantly it gives light; it dispels darkness. Physically and metaphorically, dispelling darkness, spreading light and giving warmth, is the essence of fire. Light a candle or a *diya* and keep it in your sight and trust me you will never feel alone.

Fire is the shadow of God. You look deep into fire and you glimpse God. The very human civilization dawned when mankind learnt how to make fire. Till that moment, mankind dwelled in the dark ages. It was fire that differentiated man from beast; it was fire that evolved man to his present form; it was fire that allowed mankind to even think of inventing a wheel. So son, controlled fire is enlightening and allows mankind to survive.

"How can we allow fire to help us and guide us and protect us? How can we make the external fire help the internal fire within us? Well, fire meditation is the oldest form of all meditations. It is also one of the easiest and most rewarding forms of connecting with the great Fakir, our Creator. When you light a lamp or candle, you automatically sanctify the place. The important thing to do is, light a *diya* with prayers on your lips and in your heart. Request the fire that you have just lit, to dispel darkness from your life and from the lives of your loved ones. Request the fire to spread the light of God in your lives and fill it with the warmth of God's breath.

My boy, physically and spiritually, one must have eyes to see. Most of the time, God is begging to be seen, but is ignored. Focus more and more on your God and Guru and you shall feel the presence, within and outside you as They have to be present with the disciple; it is mandatory for Them. God and Guru owe it to their children. Just as being upright, kind and noble is a must for the disciple, so God and Guru, too, are bound by rules of the ancient hermitage, where their presence is mandatory.

Thus every time you light a candle or a *diya*, a prayer to dispel darkness, physically and metaphorically, should be said. It is important. Your prayer gives a direction to the fire and the intensity of your prayer gives energy to the fire to do as directed. When you do this, the fire takes on a different intensity and proportion. Fire is used to light a cigarette and also burn down a house. By praying to the fire, you are sanctifying the process and just as you have holy water, you have created energized holy fire. You can do the same thing while lighting an incense stick. Pray that the fragrance from the incense stick, is filled with the breath of God and wherever the fragrance goes and whosoever it caresses, that being too is touched by God and is blessed with a life that is full of the fragrance and sweetness of God. Pray that the fragrance and the smoke from the incense stick cleans all that which is negative and impure; in the air, in the surroundings and mainly, within all those who inhale the fragrance. By doing this, you are giving energy and direction for only purity and Godliness to prevail, not only in the lives and minds of those touched by the light and fragrance but also in the area where the flame is lit and the incense burns. When you do this, you not only help those in the physical plane but you also help earthbound spirits to think more clearly and move on in their spiritual journey."

"All this is possible by just lighting the *diya* and the incense stick and chanting a small prayer..."

"But fuelling the prayer with intense energy and love. Yes. All this is possible. Now you are going to ask me how a person can help himself or herself with fire meditation."

"You are just impossible. You know my thoughts and you know my questions and I guess you even know my answers…"

"I am swimming in the same current as the Maker. In that current there are no secrets; no past and future; just the present and all is clear and there are no more mysteries. That is why be in prayer and be in the present and connect with this stream of vibrations and you too will be able to tap whatever you want to know about whatever there is to know. Connect your antenna properly. The show is on, all the time. Ok, now, your question…"

"That you asked…"

"Which you thought though and thus it has your energy and the question is how can one benefit from fire meditation? Does a man have to stand on one's head to get a glass of water in this stable?"

"Very funny Baba. Getting it. Would your Lordship want something else too?"

"Son, you've given me your very soul, to do what you think I deem fit. So for now, just water will do."

Rudra sighed and then nodded and with warmth spreading in his heart he went to get the old man with that wry smile and a twinkle in his eyes a glass of water.

"Light a candle or a *diya*. Preferably where you do your prayers at home. It could be a small temple or an altar or a book -shelf or whatever, make sure there is sanctity in and around the place. It need not be fancy but it should be clean and the environment around it should be appropriate. See son, a lot of families live in one room. That room is bedroom, drawing room, dining room and study room, all rolled into one. Yet, you can find some place or a wall that you can designate for your small temple or place of worship. Of course, I know of innumerable families who live in four and five bedroom apartments and still do not manage to find the right place and space for their temple and their holy flame. Sad but true and truth my son is often absurd and doesn't have to have a reason or a meaning. Anyway, my son with those long curly hair, light your flame and sit in front of it. I recommend you do this when alone and specially when it is slightly dark as then the intensity of the flame is far more. Also make certain that the flame is not flickering or dancing too much. A steady flame is what we need and that is best achieved by shutting the fan and for a while closing the door and window. Thus you sit in partial darkness and that becomes your cave and you stare at the flame, which is your fire. So you sit in front of the flame and for a while just look at it. Just see it. Observe its colours. Observe its shape. Let the flame be nice and strong. Not just some small dot of light coming out of the wick. It should be burning bright. After a minute or so, imagine you are in the flame. Fire is virtually creation and thus fire is the form of the Creator. Ancient Sages called fire, the Goddess, Devi, the Universal Mother. Imagine you are in the womb of the Universal Mother. For a while just be in Her womb. Think you safe and sound and protected in the womb of Devi, the Universal Mother; the Life Force of all creation. Then pray to Devi or the Universal Mother or the Life Force of all creation, to cleanse your body, mind and soul; aura, vibrations and channels; every drop of blood, DNA and cell, from all negativity, ill health and darkness. Tell her to remove

all darkness from your life, in your life and around your
life. Pray to the Her, to fill you up with Her warmth,
Her radiance, Her glow, Her presence and Her
protection. Tell Her to lighten up your path with her
glow so that you never go astray into darkness. If you
are feeling depressed, then pray to Her to burn away all
the gloom and depression and sadness and fill you up
with positive energy and wellbeing. If you are feeling
weak, ask Her to fill you up with strength. What ever
ails you, pray to Fire to burn it away and brighten your
life with what you feel you lack and need the most.
Continue to dwell into the Light; continue to bathe in
its pure glory. See her protective energy around you and
your aura. Her protection and energy will surround you
and your aura and thus protect you from vibrations and
negative energy that dwells around you, within you and
is projected towards you. Being in the womb of light is
a beautiful, serene and rejuvenating experience. There
will be times you will not want to come out of her

Don't for a moment think I don't get all that you keep for me. I receive
and bless all that you place before me. Sharing what you have with me
son, is all that matters to me. Share with me your joys and your pain;
your food and your doubts; your cigars and your illusions; your love
and your restlessness. I want it all. Don't keep me away from anything.
Nothing. I am you and you, my child, are I. Every child is in me and I
am in every child. I am the sunrise and the sunset. I am the moon and
the waxing and waning of it. I am fire and the light and the heat that
comes forth from it. Never, ever, distinguish me separate from matter
and mind. I am all. All are Me!

protective embrace. When you feel it is time to come out of her luminous sanctuary, then, imagine yourself returning to your body. Bow to the flame. Do a *namaste* by folding your palms together and thank Her for allowing you to connect with Her and for blessing you with her energy and protection.

"Now son, you can do this meditation not only for yourself but for your loved ones too. First connect with the flame. Be in Her womb. First say the prayer that I have told you…"

"The body, mind and soul…"

"Aura, vibrations etc. Do it first for yourself. Everything first needs cleansing and protection. After you have allowed the divine light to enter every cell in your being, then imagine your loved ones along with you in the flame too. For instance, you feel somebody is not well; you imagine that person with you in the flame and then repeat the entire prayer for that person. Ask Agni/Devi/Goddess/Fire/Divine Light to cleanse the person, fill the person with her energy and light…"

"The entire body, mind and soul prayer…"

"Despite your funny looks, you are very intelligent. Ha! Ha! Yes, do the entire prayer. That way you can keep taking up cases. But remember, whenever you pray, the most important thing to ask for is, strength and wisdom, love and compassion to accept whatever God/ Master/Destiny has in store with grace and happiness and positive surrender. This is a must. This is mandatory. Without praying this, the life force of the prayer is virtually non-existent. Whether you pray for yourself or for others, you must make sure that whatever is in store for the individual, is faced with grace, happiness and positive surrender and all these qualities can only come about if you are filled with wisdom, strength, love and compassion. If you ask me, also ask to be filled with a great sense of humour. One needs humour to go through life. Son, what I have told you now, is the simplest way of walking the path of God. It is also the surest way of reaching your destination. Fire meditation will cleanse you, nourish you, nurture you, guide you, guard you, protect you and most important of all, it shall connect your aura with the Light that originates from the Life Force. Once that connection is made, darkness caused by ignorance, hate, anger and all those accompanying emotions get burnt away in the great Divine Fire of Compassion."

"Baba, what if somebody is really in bad shape but cannot do the fire meditation? Maybe he or she can't light a candle or a *diya*; for whatever reason, then what does one do?"

"Simple. Look into the sun. Look into the morning sun. That is the best way of doing Flame meditation. There is nothing better than meditating on the rising sun. It is the source of all physical light and fire and thus the closest physical manifestation of the Divine Spark and Flame. Put yourself in the sun and follow the same prayer and routine. This is the best way of doing it. But you need to do it with the morning sun for obvious health and optical reasons. You can do it with the setting sun too. But obviously, the rising sun has great healing properties. Merging with the sun, does wonders for the body, mind, aura; it also balances your elements in your body and strengthens your magnetic field force. Your aura gets nourished and this way you get balanced and protected. Of course, all this is also achieved by fire meditation too. But if one does the meditation and prayer and merges with the morning sun the results are going to be far better, achieved faster and will be more apparent and lasting. I recommend both the methods. Some people find the flame meditation more personal and reassuring. Sitting in their dark room, with only the flame, they feel more protected and nourished. It is personal.

"The sun is the source of life and light. It gets directly nourished by the Great Flame, that we call God. The sun has nourishing and curative qualities that are not being channeled optimally. The sages knew about the power of the sun. Zoroastrians have to pray to the Sun. It is actually mandatory for them. The Hindus too have been worshiping the sun since the beginning of time. Sun temples were popular all over the world. The pyramids also harness the sun's energy, which is filtered in a calculated manner that allows energy to be preserved and keeps at bay corruption of whatever is placed within. Son, there is spiritual power and healing strengths in light: the source be it the Sun or just a flame. Also another interesting thing about fire meditation is that the moment you begin chanting prayers, you begin to bestow the Sun and the flame with further energy. Thus every time you pray to the sun or the fire, you actually through your prayers are bestowing energy to them. In return, the disciple is not only blessed with physical and material benefits but the Divine Spark, that glows in all beings, is strengthened and this in turn makes the connection between the individual Divine Spark and Cosmic Eternal Flame stronger. Thus, when you pray to the Sun or the flame, there is a bonding. Not only does the disciple receive, the disciple, through prayer, adds positive fuel and energy to the Sun and the flame. The disciple is blessed for doing this and the most beneficial blessing is bestowed: strengthening the bond between the individual's Divine Spark with the Cosmic Eternal Flame. Thus the rewards are so great that we believe fire meditation and prayers are mandatory for spiritual, physical, emotional, auric, material and mental benefits. Are you getting all this in that peculiar fat skull of yours?"

"My skull ain't fat!"

"Of course, it *ain't* fat. It is unusually thick. Now can a man smoke in this cave-like room?"

"I thought by smoking you are not giving the right respect to fire..."

"My child, with the thick head and curls, by smoking, I am always with fire. Ha! Ha! Ha!"

THE NIGHTS WERE filled with dreams and conversations. Rudra saw his children often in them. His son, always wanting to be with him, while his daughter, pretending he did not exist. Rudra saw much more and it drained

Fools try to differentiate between us. Fools succeed with fools. Be wise. Can you separate the wave from the ocean? Can the light be separated from the flame? Can you separate the sunbeams from the sun or the fire from its warmth? The fruit comes from the seed and gives seeds to get more fruit. Nature is all-encompassing and never differentiates. Only foolish mankind differentiates.

him. Most mornings, he woke up far more exhausted than when he slept. The dreams were detailed and filled with conversations. Rudra abhorred conversations in the mind. During his wakeful hours he had control over the mind and the conversations. Yes, his heart ached, all the while, but he had virtually become immune to the constant pain that throbbed with every beat.

"The only way out is to sleep for shorter periods of time. Before sleeping, chant prayers and try to meditate. Prepare your subconscious mind to relax too and be content in silence. Unlike most people, you don't indulge in thoughts and the past during your wakeful moments, that itself is very creditable my child. But that doesn't mean you don't hurt and the pain itself keeps churning within you and it is in your sleep state that the steam is let out. The churning leaves its own effect and if you don't indulge in prayers and meditation, then the body and the mind have no other way of settling the process that the pain has evoked, but through dreams. But if you notice, even in your dreams, you have never hurt anybody or been negative to anybody. That only means one thing: you really hold no hatred or malice against anybody. You are not pretending; you really have only love for all those who have hurt you and turned against you and made wrong allegations against you and tried to harm you emotionally, physically and mentally."

"Baba, before channeling, what should I do?"

"Simple. First make sure you have either had your bath or at least clean your hands, till your elbows, your feet till your ankles, your face and your neck. Also rinse your mouth and clean your ears and your nose. We call this cleansing process, *wazoo*. Always try to have a fixed time for your session; at least in the beginning. The aim is to be always in the state of meditation thus always in the state of channeling, as help might be needed anytime, anywhere, without notice. Thus, the final aim is to be in the present moment, devoid of any mental baggage, and in commune with your Master. Either in the present moment or by chanting your Master's Holy name always, one can be ready for channeling, all the time. But, initially, it is important to have one time of the day and select one particular place for channeling. Start mentally and physically detaching yourself from everything and being in prayer, long before you really sit down for channeling. Best would be to keep aside ten to fifteen minutes, for silence and meditation and chanting. The room should be closed. Light an oil lamp, *diya*, or a candle and also burn incense sticks. Create an atmosphere of sacredness and devotion. Create the same vibrations that one feels in a place of worship. Remember you are inviting your Master to come and meet you and bless you and converse with you. Make sure that the room is clean, has the fragrance of heaven and the flame of purity burning bright. If you want, before you sit down for even meditation and chanting, you can switch on a tape of chants or *bhajans* (holy songs). Then sit for

Remember, the first important rule of healing is that only God and Guru heal. Nobody else can heal. Everybody else is just a channel for healing. You, my son, are just a medium, a piano, through which the divine music flows. You are neither the musician nor the music, just the instrument. But the instrument needs to be in perfect tune and harmony.

meditation and prayer and only then sit for channeling. Just before you sit for channeling, visualize yourself in the fire and flame and seek for protection and guidance and Godliness…"

"Say the prayer you have taught…"

"What a bright fat head this child has…"

"Very funny…"

"But very astute observation from my side. Anyway, say your prayers of protection and only then sit for channeling. Sit by the fire and the lit incense stick and call out to your Master. Pray to your Master to fill your body, mind and soul; aura, vibrations, channel; every drop of blood, DNA and cell; with your Master's guidance, protection and presence. Pray to your Master to forgive you, lead you, guide you, guard you and come through you. Plead with your Master that only your Master comes through you and that your Master allows no other spirit to come even close to you. These prayers are important. The meditation and chanting are important. The flame and the incense stick are important. These are steps that make the path clear and which forms an invisible circle of protection around you, preventing any other spirit from even coming close to you. Also this circle protects you from the negativity and vibrations of those who come for channeling. Remember, only those in grief and pain shall come for channeling. They usually come with heavy auras. The medium's channels are open for communication. Many times the medium absorbs all the negativity and sorrow and heaviness; thus after the session is over, the person who has come for guidance goes back feeling relieved and light, for the simple reason he or she has unconsciously left all the pain and restless and problems at the feet of the Master; but in the process they have to pass through the feet of the medium or pass through the medium. If the medium is not protected and not in complete tune with the Master, the negativity, grief, auric heaviness clings to the medium and can result in mental turbulence, ill health, acute restlessness and emotional disorders, depression, weakness of the body, listlessness and in general, a complete physical, mental and emotional breakdown. Remember son, you are dealing with energy and energy has its own laws. If you touch a live wire without precaution and protection, you are going to get a shock. If the energy passing through the live wire is weak, you will only get a minor jolt. If the energy is strong, it can throw you off your feet and physically injure you. If you keep getting thrown off your feet and injured, after a while, you will get permanently wounded. Sometimes, the live wire has such immense energy running through it, that it can cripple you or even kill you. Energy doesn't see intentions. It has its own set of rules and the rules apply to one and all. Thus precaution and protection are a must. Also, one needs to be strong to be able to deal with energy, vibrations, auric heaviness and energy fluctuations. You need to be strong in body, mind and soul; also in complete harmony of body, mind and soul. Another point is that the Master works through you; the Master uses the medium's body to get across to those in need. If the bulb is not strong enough to absorb the electric energy passing through it, the heavy voltage can damage the bulb, crack it or even burst it. Thus, the medium had better be strong enough to bear the external turbulence and also the internal energy circuit running through his or her body. Most mediums fall ill. Most mediums suffer from innumerable problems. Many mediums become misfits in the world. All mediums suffer from physical health issues. The more in tune the medium, the greater the health issues. Saints and prophets suffer the most. Thus protection is a must. Even with protection, you are going to fall ill; suffer mental anguish and emotional burns; be drained out and have the breath sucked out of you. Sleep will go out of the window and increasingly you will get bouts of depression, as you shall be surrounded by pain and grief. Thus you shall need to be more and more immersed in prayer and in the present moment. You should learn to relax and be surrounded by happiness and laughter and indulge in what calms you. Try to be happy and as you like to say, try to be chilled out. Now after you finish channeling, first and foremost go back into your flame and pray to Her to cleanse your body, mind and soul; aura, vibrations and channels; every drop of blood, DNA and cell, from all negativity and ill health. Thank the flame for protecting you, guiding you and guarding you. Thank your Master and then if you can, burn another stick of incense or better still, burn camphor and take it through your room. You can also keep a bowl of rock salt water, and after the channeling you can flush away the water, clean the bowl and use it again when you sit for channeling. Be careful it doesn't spill on your self or in the room. If it does spill, wash it away with without delay. Irrespective of everything, you must do the *wazoo* again..."

"Cleaning the hands and feet..."

"I have a genius around me. A genius with long hair and the fattest head this side of the universe."

"Ha, ha, a very good ha. Baba, what if somebody wants to become a medium? I have you but everybody doesn't have a Saint and a Sage, who complains of tea and food and smokes and cracks sad jokes. What does the person do then?"

"I shall pretend not to have heard that but it is very important to first and foremost be in the present moment, son. It is not as easy as it seems. Then it is important to keep chanting the Master's name or being in prayer. Also one needs to be detached from one's pain and sorrows, no matter how catastrophic they may seem to be or may really be. The mind really should become still. It should be blank so that the Master can speak through. One day, the Master will speak through. Now get me your disastrous tea, which makes the mind so still that sometimes I think it doesn't even exist. Ha, Ha, a very good ha."

I remember, when your children fell ill, you would hold them close and though you didn't know it, you used to give your own energy to them; allowing them to get stronger and be able to fight the illness that had plagued their small bodies. I know how miserable you were when your children were ill. They may forget. I never shall. The Masters and nature, keeps all accounts. No love and emotion goes to waste. We receive everything and preserve it.

THEY HAD LIVED for nearly three months in the cabin by the sea. Summer was round the horizon, what with the rain-drenched clouds, virtually all packed and ready to travel to other parts of the world. Rudra lay on the sofa, virtually dead with exhaustion. He felt as though somebody had switched off the supply of power and oxygen to his body. He felt sapped of energy and his body hurt, just as it used to, when he would go for those long walks in the mountains, as a child.

Baba had disappeared once again. He had subtly warned Rudra that this time he would be gone for a longer duration of time. There was a lot to do and each moment lost, meant that the chance of saving a soul from self-destruction got weaker and dimmer. Baba often insisted that most of the time, pain and sorrow were self-inflicted. Yes, very often, the mechanics of karma caught up with the individual and grief, misfortune and tragedy reigned but most often, the individual seeing the ditch in front, would yet insist of walking straight into it, fall, get bruised, injured or bedridden and then blame Providence, destiny and even doubt often, the very existence, essence or justice of the Creator, for letting the calamity take place. What calamity? Most often, we are stark raving stupid. We shut our eyes to the obvious. As the Bible says, nobody is as blind as the person who refuses to see. The world is filled with such blind folk. We all are blind sometime in our lives but many insist on seeing the world with their eyes tight shut and just in case they fear they might open their eyes by mistake, they even glue them shut with some prejudice or the other.

Destiny is a road map that points out the general

direction, major destinations and gives an overview of the journey to be undertaken. Avoiding potholes, bad roads and speed breakers and using common sense are at the discretion of the driver. Very often the driver can't differentiate his ass from the steering wheel.

RUDRA BREATHED IN deep and slowly got to his feet. There was one more case to be handled. There were days he sat for channeling for a few hours. Some days, he had nobody calling him. What was really strange was that before Baba had left, he had called Rudra to the room and asked him to sit down.

"You are a medium. Always remember this. You are not the doer but the channel through which energy and the breath of God flows. For a moment do not entertain any illusion that you have power or are spiritually on a higher plane just because you have been chosen to be a medium. You have a gift, just like a pianist has the talent for composing or playing music. That makes neither you nor the pianist spiritually any higher or lower than your brother cleaning the garbage by the roadside. The energy and breath of our Lord flows through all; ant to angels; thus what is important is our you using or abusing that energy and breath of our Creator, Sarkar, Fakir, Old Man, Goddess, Universal Mother, God, Allah, Zarathushtra, Ram, Ahura, Sai, Meher... Whatever you wish to call Him or Her. Secondly, don't charge anything. I am not saying its right or wrong to charge. All I am saying is you don't charge anything. If somebody wants to give you something, tell that person to place it at the altar. If it is money, of that use some of it to help the needy and the remaining to keep your body and soul together. But never ever ask or charge or even expect anything. Charity and nobility lose their spiritual essence if any personal gain is attached to it. There may be some who will not offer a flower at the altar and some who will place gold. All are the same to you. All are to be given the same importance. All come to the Lord and not you, never, ever, forget that. Don't expect to be given any importance or leeway just because you spend your time in the service of mankind. You are doing nobody a favour but yourself as you are working on your karma and in the process helping your evolution too. Yes, the more you serve selflessly, without being concerned about your own karmic growth or any sort of gain, but doing so because that is what you have to do and want to do, with no strings attached and expecting nothing in return, not even personal safety, of body, mind and soul, but leaving all to the Master, then you are walking a different path and we are talking about dancing to a different beat. That's a different scenario altogether and you have a reached a lighter dimension and in that dimension a lot is unsaid and unseen but only experienced. Work and live to annihilate your little petty ego and bask in the glory and presence of your Master, God and Goddess.

"Sometimes when an accident or a tragedy takes place and either the individual or the individual's family and friends are saved from the tragedy that may have resulted in the death of many others, usually we hear the individual saying 'God is great, I was saved or not one member of my family came to harm'. Would God not be great if the individual or a family member would have come to harm? I've heard people saying my

Master's hand was on my head thus nothing happened to me. Does that mean those who were injured did not have their Masters' hand and blessings on their head? Or does that mean your Master is more powerful than their Master or your prayers more heard than those who suffered? When a tragedy, say like the tragedy where in a bomb blast two hundred innocent people have died or got maimed, while some have escaped unharmed or were not present when the blast occurred, there is huge karma and destiny at play. The Master might change your karma and destiny if He or She feels that is for your larger good. So you might be saved despite all odds and a miracle takes place. Yes that is your Master's doing. But remember, sometimes the Master works another sort of miracle; a miracle in reverse. The Master knowing well that the individual has a long life, but a life now fraught with pain and humiliation might instead cut short your lifespan. So in the tragedy, which the individual should have survived but been bedridden or been distraught or died everyday, the Master works a miracle by cutting short the misfortune and pain lying ahead, by taking away the individual to a secure place where pain and humiliation have no place or power to affect the person. So the person dies in the bomb blast or accident or whatever. The person does so with the

Take any Master and if you ask His or Her disciple, you will be told how unwell the Master is virtually all the time. Why? Because the Master consciously keeps taking on the karma and illnesses of the disciples and devotees and thus illnesses plague spiritual Masters.

Master's blessings. Isn't that a miracle too? The Masters
are working round the clock for those who work for
Them on the physical and spiritual plane. Work for
Them, not only by being mediums but by serving
mankind or by just being upright, compassionate, loving
human beings. Those who serve their Masters are served
a million times more by their Masters. You serve first
and foremost by being a decent human being. You serve
by not harming others and by not gossiping and plotting
and trying to create sadness and an environment of hate
and pain. You serve by not alleging and trying to break
families. Yes, you also serve by being a medium; by doing
social work; by being generous; by giving a helping hand;
by reaching out to the unfortunate or the unprivileged,
by praying for peace and health for those who are in
need for peace and health; for meditating for world
peace; for feeding the hungry and clothing those in need
and providing shelter to the homeless. There are a million
ways to serve God, Goddess and your Master but always
remember your Master sees and appreciates and serves
you back a million times more. Another thing, you must
have so much faith in your Guru and Master that your
faith overwhelms your Master too but to reach such a
level, you will be tested, cleansed, crucified, humiliated,
injured, wiped out, stranded...it's not an easy thing to
overwhelm your Guru with your faith. Your faith should
be such that even your Master gets shaken up but my
child to shake your Master up, you should be ready to
have the very foundations beneath you and the sky above
you to be shaken up and your body, mind and soul and
the world around you to be traumatized. You want to
give a gift to your Master then give your Master your

very soul and you know what is the essence of the soul...it is faith. Faith is the heartbeat that keeps the soul pure and intact in its original glory despite having been put through lifetimes of depravity and darkness. Faith keeps God from pulling the plug off from creation. Love and faith are two sides of eternity."

RUDRA SIGHED AND sat on the sofa. He lit a cigar and inhaled deep. A German couple had presented it to Rudra just before they had flown back to London where they had lived for nearly six decades. Two weeks back they had come to Rudra because their passports had been stolen. Rudra had shut his eyes and waited for an answer. Then he had opened his eyes and smiled.

"The passport is in your suitcase. It's in a plastic bag which is in the inner pocket of a coat; a maroon coat. If you find your passport I want you to donate a little money to charity. Make sure it helps children or those suffering from cancer."

Rudra thought the old man would pass out. The old lady, with a thick voice and eyes that were light red in colour, smiled. Yes, she remembered, she had kept something in the maroon coat but had forgotten about it and don't worry about the old man who was still on the verge of passing out, he did not believe in all this, thus reality had socked him in the solar plexus. You know how stubborn and stupid men can be about love and God. Next day they arrived with wine and cigars. They had noticed packets of cigarettes and had seen him drinking wine at that strange café with atrocious waiters but excellent food.

"Why did Baba ask us to donate money to help children or those suffering from cancer?"

"Maybe because a grandchild of yours is not keeping good health or somebody in the family is liable to get cancer!"

The old man coughed and for a while in the room, only irregular breathing from the old man was heard.

"My grandson is very accident prone. In the past one year he has been involved in four accidents..."

"Maybe Baba wants you to thank the Lord for protecting your grandson from perpetual harm or by helping the children, Baba is trying to settle certain karmic accounts..."

"How?"

"By helping people, in this case children, you kind of settle karmic debts. Nature and providence keeps all scores and accounts. Maybe by helping children, blessings from the souls of these children, consciously or subconsciously, blessings from the spirits who take care of these orphaned children, and blessings from your own Guides and Masters, helps to erase certain karmic debts and punishments. It also helps in preventing coming tragedy or misfortune or helps in the recovery of somebody suffering. It is also a way of thanking Providence."

"You know before we came to India, our son-in-law, Philip, was suspected of having cancer of the stomach... It was a close call. The doctors have prescribed him life long medication and a complete change of lifestyle..."

"Maybe by giving charity to an organization that takes care of cancer patients, this is a way of thanking the Lord."

The old man stood up. It was obvious he, too, wanted to say something and for a few seconds floundered for words. Rudra stood up too and held the man by his arm. The old man with a face that did not give in to emotion often, softened and he looked at his wife first and then Rudra.

"All my life I have spent every given opportunity trying to ridicule those who believed in the power of prayer, miracles, healing and anything supernatural. What a fool I have been. What a blind fool. God have mercy on my soul."

The old lady stood up and smiled. A strange smile it was. Not a smile indicating victory. Not a smile that reeked of ego. It was a smile that radiated relief and happiness that one often notices in a mother who sees her wayward child coming home, walking the right path.

"Love, it's never ever late to awaken to the glory of God."

It's not that They could not cure Themselves, They could, but there are certain laws of energy and karma and They abided by those laws. If Jesus wasn't ready to be crucified, do you really believe any man on earth or any force in the Universe could have managed to touch a hair on His head, leave aside make Him wear a crown of thorns or crucify Him? No. He allowed it to happen. He wanted to take on the cumulative karma of mankind. He took these on to Himself and thus allowed Himself to go through pain-agony-abuse that only Masters can go through for their children. And all this made all the more painful, for the Master can stop or shield Himself from feeling pain, but He doesn't, as that interferes with His plan and the law of karma.

So they sat on the veranda, sipped red wine, smoked cigars and then had a grand dinner of eggs, cheese, whole wheat bread and lots of tinned tuna. All the while, Rudra observed the slow transformation of a man from a cynic to a lover of God. That night, plans for charity were made and Rudra witnessed first hand the manner in which Baba had made him instrumental in the spread of light and joy; not only in the lives of these two elderly people but also in the lives of so many children and those suffering from a disease that had destroyed the lives of millions all over the world. He understood what Baba had meant by saying that each individual can make a difference that could have a ripple effect on the lives of countless individuals. With this couple basking in the light of God, Rudra realized that innumerable children and ailing people would be helped and the chain had begun and light would be passed on, long after Rudra and the old couple would leave their physical shells and travel light in light.

Rudra walked towards the water, cigar in the mouth, long hair flowing with the wind. Many of the dogs who now had become friendly with this loner, ran towards him, wagging their tails and walking by his side while he lovingly caressed a few of them and called all of them ' hello my sweet S.O.Bs'.

RUDRA SAT IN Baba's room, in front of the lit flame. Two sandalwood incense sticks burned and their earthy fragrance could be whiffed even outside the room. Rudra sat with eyes focused on the flame. The room was dark and the flame's golden glow was all the more luminous and enchanting. Rudra prayed for protection and guidance. Any moment Chavan would arrive to seek answers and solutions. Rudra, for the life of him, couldn't understand, from where and how people got to know about his channeling. It was as though some force in the universe made sure that people kept coming over to the small cabin by the sea, surrounded by coconut and palm trees and lived in by a sage who spoke to nobody and the long haired man who seemed all washed up but yet perfectly content with his lot.

Rudra heard the shuffle of feet and Chavan entered the room. Rudra had the bandana on his head and nodded to the middle aged man. After another short silent prayer, Rudra waited for the energy to fill him up. It was a warm inexplicable sensation and till Rudra did not feel the energy within him, he remained silent.

"Your sadness and frustrations are of your own doing. If you go deep within yourself, you will realize that you have created your own sorrows. You possess everything but enjoy nothing. You are surrounded by people all the time but are terribly lonely. You are falling ill and feel aches and pains all over the body all the time but nothing's medically wrong with you. You want to expand your business and are on the verge of diversifying. It's not a very good idea. You will make lots of money but money you already possess in abundance. Making more money is nothing but a

Remember, the law of nature works in simple ways; somebody has to absorb whatever energy is set loose. Somebody has to foot the bill. Whether the individual pays or the Master, the law of nature and karma is not really interested.

statistic. It's just another million or crore. Nothing wrong in making more money but if that money is not going to give you any happiness but instead create more confusion and ill health then that money is harmful. So I don't think you should go for that expansion. Now you ask me, whatever you want to."

"My main issue is my family. They just don't relate to me. My sons are not interested in my work. My wife seems distant and I just have nobody to communicate with."

"Communication is a two way street son. When was the last time you really sat down with your family and enjoyed yourself? Your phone never stops ringing. Your moods are controlled by your balance sheet and your work schedule. Your plans to spend time with your family are solely dependent to your moods and state of work. You expect all to be present at home when you are there but your schedule is so erratic that you yourself are not certain whether you shall be present at home at a given time and date. Your son needs a father and a friend. He has somebody who only judges him, sets parameters and compares him with other children of his age."

"I only want what is best for him..."

"Wrong. You want what you think is best for him. Tell me do you really know what your son wants to do or is capable of doing?"

"I...uh...I want him to join my work..."

"Do you know what he want to do or dreams of doing or what he is meant to do?"

Chavan nodded. He had begun to question the wisdom behind his agreeing for this session.

"Your son wants to become an engineer. Just like you wanted to but couldn't because of family pressure. Your son wants to go abroad and study and make his own destiny. You couldn't make your own destiny so I assume you want to deprive your children from charting out their destiny..."

"They don't listen to me..."

"That is because you are a stranger to them and you don't listen to them. Your daughter who is thirteen is slowly getting distant from you and you are at fault. Your wife, seeing the way you are interacting with your children has begun to slowly close herself to you. Son, you have come here to hear the truth. You have not come here to hear what you want to hear. You shall hear the truth or leave..."

"No, no. I agree to whatever you are saying. I don't know what to do."

Suddenly a tenderness engulfed Rudra. He could feel his gaze and tone become softer. More tender.

"I want you to tell me what is your priority in life. Shut your eyes and think and tell me, what is your priority. Forget everything else, just tell me your main priority in your life and after you ascertain your priority tell me what are you doing to work towards your priority. But be honest with yourself. If money is your priority, there is nothing to feel bad about. Then you should ascertain whether you are doing your best to

The karmic accountant can be convinced to change the address of billing but the bill has to be sent and paid for; somebody has to foot the bill. The karma has to be worked upon.

achieve that priority. But be honest with yourself. Now shut your eyes and think."

Rudra knew the answer. He shut his eyes to and tried to figure out, what was his priority and was he doing his darn all and giving his best to work towards his priority? After a while, he heard Chavan move about on his chair. Rudra opened his eyes and was taken aback to see that Chavan's eyes had welled up. The rich tycoon, who had at least a hundred people at his beck and call, now sat in front of Sai Baba's frame, a glowing flame and an unshaven man in jeans and a bandana, unsure and humbled by whatever revelation his soul had divulged to him.

"What is your priority?"

"My family."

"Do you really mean it?"

"Yes."

"I mean, do you really mean and believe that your family is your priority?"

"Yes! I just realized that without them everything is meaningless to me. They mean the world to me and life without them would be rubbish."

"I believe you that your family is your priority. Now tell me, what are you doing about your priority? Are you giving your best to your family? Are you doing all that which is possible to improve the quality of their life? If tomorrow you were to die, would you die in peace, knowing you have done your level best and given your level best towards your priority? If your answer is yes, then you will leave your body in peace. If your answer is no, even in the spirit plane and world, you will carry a cross and the guilt and anger towards yourself, which is not good for one's spiritual journey and growth. You carry those feelings in your afterlife and in all your other lives too. A feeling of sadness that you cannot pinpoint but which fills your soul with a void that engulfs you. Son, if your family is your priority then work towards giving your best to them. Their welfare becomes your priority. Their wellbeing and state of mind becomes your priority. To make certain that they flower and reach their potential as human beings and in their career and in their lives becomes your priority. What is the sense of expanding your business at the cost of your family and your priority? It's important to run the race but stupidity to keep running even after the finishing line has been crossed. Draw your finishing line and try to cross it but keep your priority in mind and work at it continuously.

"Priority means that which is the most important thing for you and your soul and your peace of mind. For you, your family is top priority. For somebody else,

The Guru comes before God. God has laid down the laws and thus God too is bound by those very laws and remember God is all Just. God cannot be lenient to some and unsparing to others; unless the case is presented by the Guru. When the Guru seeks for karmas to be changed or altered, God consents. The Guru is like a mother; all merciful and with a heart that beats and bleeds for the disciples. The Master thus bends the laws for the peace and happiness of the disciples; but the Guru pays a price that is so excruciating that nobody can decipher or comprehend.

art or money may be top priority. The question to be asked is whether you are working towards your priority? Are you giving your thousand percent to your priority? Are you giving top priority to your priority? If the answer to these questions is honest and you are doing your best, then great! Let not the outcome decide whether you are moving towards your priority. For instance, a person's priority may be to keep his or her family happy but the person sees only sadness and hatred in their eyes. That is unfortunate but as long as the person is trying his or her best to make them happy and content and is working towards that priority that is all that matters. For a person, art may be priority but the person may be a failure at art but as long as the person yet gives his or her thousand percent towards art, that is all that matters. But be honest in ascertaining what your priority is and then work towards it. A person can have family and work as priority. Then work towards both of them. Don't sacrifice one for the other. Create a situation where you are giving your best to both. Very difficult but it is achievable. Work towards them and devote your life towards your priority."

"How could I have been so stupid as to not have seen this? I mean, how could I have not figured it out myself? I would have saved my family and myself so much grief. You are right. I have made myself a stranger to my family but I expect them to behave as family to me. First I need to be family to them and then expect any real bonding. God bless you. Really. God bless you. How can I thank you? Tell me. What can I do for you?"

"Its not me. It's Sai Baba of Shirdi. I'm nothing. I'm just His ash. Baba says keep aside a fixed percentage of whatever you earn for the poor. Two percent or five percent of your net profit, keep for the poor. You can start a small trust to help children get better education and medical assistance. Just help people. That is the best way you can thank God for all that God has done for you and your family. For all that which God has bestowed on you and your family, help those in need. You want to show your gratitude to God then help those in need. Just give and give and give and help those in need."

"COME IN."

A family of three walked in. The couple were in their mid forties. Young, rich, well groomed and it was clear they had travelled and shopped all over the world. Their daughter was beautiful and seemed amused on seeing Rudra. Most people were taken aback or surprised when they realised that Rudra was a channel. He was not the typical medium. Most people expected an old man with a long beard and white hair. Instead they saw a young man in jeans and long hair. They expected to meet a sage and instead were introduced to a hippie.

Rudra switched off and prayed for guidance and protection. He was really tired. He had sat through seven

Fill my body, mind and soul; auras, vibrations and channels; every drop of blood, DNA and cell; my entire being, with your protection, love, guidance, strength, healing energies, spiritual energies and grace; forgive me, lead me, guide me, guard me and have mercy on me.

sessions and now he could feel his body and mind protest.

"All of a sudden things are not going on well for you."

"Yes. Till last year things were really going smoothly but now since eight months we have been experiencing one problem after the other."

"You had given a promise to your Goddess that if certain things did take place you would go on a pilgrimage to meet Her. You would take your entire family."

"No. I don't believe in taking such pledges."

Rudra shut his eyes and prayed to Baba. He got the same answer. He also saw flashes of legal papers and a clock ticking.

"I see legal papers and a clock ticking. Does that make any sense to you?"

The woman gasped aloud. The man sat upright. The daughter for the first time looked interested.

"You had promised the Goddess that if you all were spared from certain legal enquiries, which could have destroyed your reputation in your business, you would take the entire family to Vaishno Devi and you would, in fact, shave off all the hair on your head."

"My God! My God! My God! Yes. Yes. Yes. How could I have forgotten?"

"I think Devi even tried to remind you of your promise by making certain that you began to lose your hair and in fact you have lost substantial hair growth since the past year and a half."

"Oh is that why I'm losing hair? Damn!"

"Rajesh mind your language."

"Sorry. Sorry. Sorry. No offence. You are so bloody...I mean you are so darn right. I had promised Her that if our name did not come in a particular legal enquiry we would all go to Her and prostrate ourselves and I would shave my hair and only then return to our home. I must have taken the promise a few years back. You are trying to tell me that whatever is happening to me at work is because I forgot my pledge?"

"Yes."

"That's not fair..."

"Don't talk about being fair. You come down very hard on your defaulters. You have often shown little mercy on those who owe you money! Be grateful that the Goddess has not shown the same ruthlessness to you that you show to those who have defaulted or gone back on their word to you."

It was a very awkward moment. Rudra was stunned by his tone and the words that came out from him. He did not want to sound blunt but he was as diplomatic as a category five hurricane. The man's face had turned red with anger and embarrassment but for some odd reason, his wife seemed very amused. She had a broad smile on her face.

"You will have to excuse my husband. He is not used

Please heal this child's body, mind and soul; auras, vibrations, channel; every drop of blood, DNA and cell but If for whatever reason the child has to go through the illness and the experience of the illness, please give the child, wisdom, strength, love and compassion to go through the illness and experience with grace, positive surrender and even happiness.

to being talked to the way you have, as he makes it a point to surround himself with as many 'yes men' as is humanly possible. We will go as soon as possible, please assure Baba. I want to ask you..."

"You mean you want to ask Baba..."

"Yes. Sorry. I want to ask Baba if we can send our daughter to the US..."

"Not till she reaches the age of nineteen. She is very accident -prone and she could meet with a major accident. This land is good for her."

"Yes, she is accident prone. In fact, just last week she banged her brand new Honda..."

"It wasn't my fault..."

"Baba knows it wasn't your fault. He also has saved you last year from another accident..."

"Oh, yeah. I could have died that time."

"You shall turn eighteen in a short while..."

"Next month..."

"That means you have to wait for another year. Its better you hold on."

The young girl looked at Rudra. Then she turned towards her parents.

"Ok. I'll wait till I turn nineteen."

Her mother was shocked. The father looked at his daughter with eyes wide in disbelief. Obviously, the girl had a mind of her own, which she did not hesitate to speak out. She must be a handful when she wanted to dig her feet into the ground.

"She should concentrate on designing. She is good at that. Either designing or law."

"They want me to do MBA. That is their condition for sending me abroad. I want to do design jewellery."

"Let her do designing. She will make a name as well as find fulfillment. I would also suggest you go to Vaishno Devi immediately…"

"She has been telling us about this designing jewellery course. But we aren't certain."

"Let her focus on designing. It will do her good. She will pursue her gift even after marriage. She will marry when she reaches twenty-seven…"

"Twenty-seven! That's too late…"

"It's best you wait till she reaches that age. Or else she could have a turbulent few years of marriage. Anyway you folks plan your trip to Vaishno Devi…"

"We can't go till next month as we are traveling to France on Friday. Can we postpone it till we return?"

"Okay but at least go to the Devi temple your family has been frequenting for years and assure the Goddess that you will go to Vaishno Devi on your return. Also, before you leave for France, try and feed poor people…"

"Can we give money to an old people's home? They accept grain and they cook for the old people living there. Also we can supply food grain to the Home which could last them for a month or more."

"That's fine. Anything more?"

"Please tell Baba to take care of our daughter. She really is accident prone."

Rudra was made to pick up the ash that had collected from the innumerable burnt incense sticks. The ash had collected in a bowl. Rudra scooped out a little and after a short prayer handed it to the young girl.

"Put this ash in a small red cloth. Carry it in your purse. Make sure it is with you whenever you leave the house. Will you do that?"

"Sure."

"Keep it with you till you reach your nineteenth birthday. Then, if you want, you can put it to sea or continue carrying it with you."

The girl smiled and did a *namaste*. Her mother touched Rudra's feet. The man nodded and left the room.

After Rudra was alone, he continued to stare into the flame. He said his prayer for cleansing and protection, thanked Baba and then removed the bandana. He was exhausted. He needed a smoke real bad!

For more than an hour, he lay on the sofa, on the veranda and stared at the sea. One of the dogs that Rudra had named, Blondie, approached him, stared at him with love for a while, sighed and then lay by the sofa. Both man and dog stared at the sea. One reflected on mankind. The other enjoyed the beauty of nature.

RUDRA DREADED WHAT lay ahead. He did not want to know the truth but was already aware of it. Seth sat near the young girl who seemed to have aged considerably in the past nine weeks. She stared straight ahead, into Sai Baba's eyes. Rudra breathed in deep and waited for the energy to flow through him and use his body, mind, breath and soul to channel Baba's words and energy.

Seth had met him the night before and informed Rudra that Jeevan, Seth's nephew had died a week earlier. Jeevan's car had skidded and collided with a bus. Jeevan had died on the spot. There had been no other casualty. All those who had been present were shocked at the freakishness of the accident. It had taken precisely fourteen seconds for the entire misfortunate incident. By the end of those few seconds, Jeevan had already left his physical body. Rudra rued the futility of it all. The absurdness of existence and the cruel detached execution of fate. To make certain a child grew up to be a happy, healthy, decent human being, so much of love, energy, heartache, planning, sacrifice, sleeplessness nights, constant tenderness and perpetual anxiety for years and years and years were required, all of it to be snuffed out in just fourteen seconds; for no fault of either the parents, the family, the lover but because for some odd reason the car skidded and crashed into an oncoming bus. Did fourteen seconds have greater depth than over two decades of selfless love? All the years of devotion and dedication, love and tears, heartaches and sheer unadulterated joy were not able to wipe out those miserable fourteen seconds and prevent the collision! Creation did not make much sense, so often. Yes, Rudra was certain that there was a perfectly logical reason in the books of fate and destiny, to justify the fourteen seconds, but as the book of fate and destiny were written in a language that only the good author of that controversial book could read and understand, there wasn't great consolation. The fact of the matter is *fate* is a four-letter word. Include *life* and *love* too in that

"Give Providence a reason to help you and the best way is to convince the Universe that you are going to take care of the needy and the sick and hungry and the damned".

controversial list. One needs great love, compassion, a very weird sense of humour, wisdom and courage to go through life with grace and without bitterness, embracing the will and wishes of the Master; thanking God and really meaning it.

Rudra looked at Sonal. She still looked like a child. She couldn't be more than twenty. Life had flung acid on her and destiny had tried to wrap up the wound with cloth dripping with salt.

"He was supposed to live through the accident." Rudra could feel Baba's presence pulsating through him. The energy vibrated within him and it made Rudra connect with all of creation. It was a strange feeling. It was virtually intoxicating and lot more overpowering. "Jeevan was supposed to live for another fifty years. In his astrological chart, he is supposed to drop the physical body at the age of seventy-eight. But what has not been mentioned in the astrological chart, is that, for more than fifty years he was to spend every moment of it, on bed, paralyzed and with many health issues, all resulting from the accident and compounded by paralysis. Jeevan understood that. He understood it four days before he died. He mentioned it to you."

The young girl with eyes that seemed to be lost in the pool of tears and waves of torment nodded in the affirmative. She wanted to speak but could not. Her throat was choked. Her tears kept flowing. Her breathing was erratic. She kept shaking her head from side to side and did not even realize that she was doing it. She kept taking deep gulps of breath and exhaled even harder. The poor girl was distraught and devastated.

"His guru, Swami Akalkoth Maharaj, came to Jeevan

in his dreams, on the fortieth day after he had begun two hours of daily prayer, burning oil lamps all through the day and of doing lots more of charity than what the Master had even asked him to indulge in. We had told the boy to give five percent to charity. He gave ten percent. He has adopted twenty-five orphans in Kashmir and his Trust along with a trust in Kashmir, will take care of the lodging, food, clothing, medicine and education of these children till they complete their graduation. The blessings Jeevan has got from the children and the family of these children, those alive and those in the spirit world, helped Jeevan a million times more. Swami Akalkoth Maharaj, Jeevan's Guru, took care of the rest. He has taken Jeevan away to a place that is filled with tenderness, compassion, love and the ability of growing spiritually and helping all those living in the physical plane and in the spiritual planes. Jeevan has also left you with all that he had ever earned or profited or saved. The money he has put in certain bonds that will take care of you and your family for the rest of your life. We shall allow you to grieve for a while but you must understand that you have come here for a purpose. To take care of those suffering and you shall spend the rest of your life taking care of children who are suffering from accidents and paralysis, as by taking care of them, you will be taking care of

Don't expect to be given any importance or leeway just because you spend your time in the service of mankind. You are doing nobody a favour but yourself as you are working on your karma and in the process helping your evolution too.

your love and you shall feel closer to Jeevan through the process of *seva*; serving those in need, is serving God. For you, your God is your love. By serving the disabled and those suffering, you shall be serving and honouring your love. We have taken care of your financial needs for life now. Jeevan has taken care of you. Now you take care of Jeevan. See him in all those who are injured and those who suffer and show your love towards him by showing your love towards all those who need help, care and support.

"Jeevan is with you. If you do not get a grip on your emotions he will be forced to be with you and he shall grieve a hundredfold as your sorrow shall pull him down and drown him with your vibrations. But if you use your pain and grief by serving those who are in need, Jeevan will always be with you. He too will be able to grow spiritually, and he too will be able to heal those who suffer and this he will do through you. But for that you shall have to be open and you can only be open when anger, bitterness, hatred, despondent gloom do not rule you. Grieving and hurting are natural processes of healing. But one needs to do that without bitterness and anger. Nobody expects you to be happy and chirpy for a long time. That is fine. As long as you don't grieve with anger and hatred and with a sense of being a victim, you are on the right path. Nobody is a victim. There are no preys and no hunters. Fill yourself up with God and selfless love and you shall be the shadow of God. Fill yourself up more with the Creator and after a while you will merge in God. Fill yourself further with the Maker and a time shall come when you too shall become God, as there shall be no difference between you and your Maker. Like the waves in the ocean, you too shall become the ocean. Just serve in the best way you can serve. We called Jeevan here so that he could initiate the process of *seva* and you could complete the process he has begun. Be true to yourself and to your love. Your man would not have liked it any other way. If you are at peace, then he is at peace. You can be sad and yet in peace. You can be happy and yet filled with conflict. Don't fight grief but certainly don't push away the sense of peace that comes when you are with your Maker and helping those who need help."

She looked at Baba's frame and then at Rudra.

"I can't breathe. I can't live without him. I want to die and go to him. I want to die. I feel I am going to kill myself…"

"Killing yourself won't guarantee your meeting him, dear child. If anything, killing yourself will assure that you don't meet him, forever. Remember, when a person kills himself or herself, the soul goes through its own trauma. The reason why the person committed suicide follows the soul in the spirit world too. Suppose a person kills herself in a fit of anger. For whatever reason, in anger, the person commits suicide and leaves the physical body. Now just because the person has left the physical

Whoever the Master really loved went through greater suffering and anguish. Those who the Master had chosen as His very own and the Master wanted to clear their karmic account, or cleanse the person off the karmic baggage, or to complete the person's karmic balance sheet and keep the child with the Master in the spirit plane, were the ones who went through the greatest hardship and obstacles.

body it does not mean the emotions and the overpowering sense of rage are no longer felt. The mind doesn't cease to exist. Thought process doesn't stop. Emotions still lash and create their own actions and reactions. The greatest myth is that death puts an end to all suffering. Yes, death puts an end to all suffering related with the body and circumstances. Yes, if a person suffered from cancer and for years was distraught with pain and agony, for sure death puts an end to the pain and suffering. But if a person was consumed with anger and rage for being inflicted with a fatal illness; then after death, the physical pain of the illness would cease, but the mental, emotional and spiritual angst and anger and negativity would still be carried over. The person will have to make an effort to let go of the negativity. If he or she doesn't, then the soul can be earth-bound. The person would be neither at peace in the spiritual plane nor at peace on earth. An extremely unpleasant situation to be in and till the anger and negativity is not converted to love and compassion, the soul remains in limbo. By limbo, we mean a state of stagnation and rot. It means a state where disintegration and further chaos reigns. It's more a state of mind, than some sort of a spiritual zone. So what I am trying to explain to you is that suicide is of no use. If you think you are miserable now, you have no idea how miserable you are going to be after your soul is forced to leave its body by the act of suicide. Child, just keep chanting your Guru's name. Yes, I know I am your Guru. Your family has come often to Shirdi and prostrated themselves at my Feet. Just keep me in your mind and thoughts and heart and soul, all the time. The more you think of me, the more I shall reside within you. The more you try to come closer to me, the nearer I come to you. You take a step towards me I shall walk a mile towards you. I am always with those who remember me and chant my name through happiness and sorrow. I am always with you, my child; your Shirdi Sai Baba is always with you, so never ever worry. Don't try to fight the sorrow. You shall have to live with it all your life. The intensity of the pain might fluctuate but the ache will always be there but that doesn't matter. You just keep walking on the path of self-realization, Guru Love, and service to all."

Baba then, through Rudra, explained fire meditation and also gave the girl the prayer of protection of body, mind and soul. Before leaving, the girl embraced Rudra, like a child would her father. Rudra felt a thousand years old.

An hour later Rudra fell ill. Fever, depression, restlessness and total collapse of the body plagued him for the next three days. Rudra was alone through those days. He lay on his mattress or slept collapsed on the veranda sofa and saw the sea and the sky and got up only to feed his three dogs. They made it a point that either all of them or at least one of them was with Rudra through the days of illness. On the fourth day, when

All answers are within each individual. All the individual needs to do is sit silently and go within. Focus on one's breath and slowly begin the journey back to one's real home. For that one needs no medium, no ashram, no books, no pseudo master, just faith that your real Master is within you and is eager to guide you back home.

Rudra woke up, he realized he felt much better and then noticed the three dogs frolicking on the beach. Blondie saw him and from far barked out a yelp of happiness.

Rudra sighed and for the first time in days ventured out on the beach. It was still early in the morning and it was relatively cool outside. He walked towards his pack of friends and they ran towards him with unmasked joy, as though, meeting a friend after years and years of separation.

RUDRA WONDERED ABOUT life after death. He was supposed to meet a man who had just lost his son in a train accident. The man lived in the city but a friend of his, Deshmukh, owned a grocery store near by. Rudra had promised the grocer, that he would see this father who mourned for his dead son, this week. Deshmukh had pleaded that the sooner Rudra saw his friend, Wadhwani, the better it would be, as the man was sinking. He had stopped all business activity. His wife feared for his health, which was getting worse by the day.

"He wants to speak to his son, Rudra Saab, so please help him out."

"I don't know if that is possible. I mean, I have never communicated with souls..."

"I have heard a lot about you saab. I know you can help him. He has gone to many mediums, but he doesn't seem to be convinced that he spoke to his son. Something tells me you can help my friend. He is really ruined. His son was everything to him."

No amount of convincing worked with Deshmukh.

So in the end Rudra agreed, only after the soft voice within him, consented to the meeting.

"Baba, where are you? You old man I miss you."

All through the day, Rudra managed to conserve his strength. He had never felt this weak all his life. The sessions were taking a toll on his health. He could feel his body ache and his energy level struggle to keep afloat. Baba had told him often that 'light work', spread light around, but often engulfed the channel in the darkness of ill health and mental fatigue. Rudra wondered how Baba managed it. He was aware that the old man was ill, weak and consumed with pain that had no particular genesis but was consistent and overwhelming.

THERE WAS NO news from Baba. Three weeks had passed since the old man had once again disappeared to save some poor sod, 'just the same way the old man had saved me', concluded Rudra. The channeling had begun again. Rudra, though much weaker, had learnt how to conserve his failing strength. He took people at intervals and during the hiatus he indulged in reading, watching sitcoms that made him laugh and avoiding the memories of his children or the cases that came to Baba, through him.

He had been shocked when, for the first time, he had opened the envelopes that people left at the altar for the channeling sessions, and found that there was enough to pay three months rent. If things went on like this, Rudra could be with Baba in this beautiful cabin till March next year. It was still September. September meant his daughter's birthday. It was for that reason Rudra did not call for newspapers and had torn the month of September and November from the calendar. In November, his son was born. Two months, that had meant the world to him, and now he looked upon them with dread. For years, he had loved the days preceding the birthdays of his children. Now he fell into graveyard depressions. Thus, he had worked out a plan. He would abstain from knowing the dates of the entire month. If he didn't know the date and was unaware of their birthdays, then the chance of him hurting so much was reduced considerably. Just reduced though, never obliterated. It was strange how pain never disappeared when the love was true and selfless. It just got deeper and more permanent. It ate into one's very being but Rudra knew for certain, that when all of them had left the physical plane, they would be reunited in the spirit world and be together forever and ever more. The truth would be known and he would be set free. He was certain of that and the thought of forever being together and growing spiritually together gave him a small measure of solace.

But Rudra wondered whether his children missed him on their birthdays. Did they miss him at all or had they believed all the muck spewed against him and all the facts that had been distorted to prove he was not their loving dad but a monster in disguise? He had been their mother and father for eleven years. Had given them his very soul. Would his love match up to the hatred and venom spewed out against him? He had heard from cases similar, that often children forgot all the love and succumbed to the brain washing.

Rudra chewed on the cigar and inhaled deep. It was

late at night. He was in his room. Only golden coloured flames and the shimmering tip of the cigar played with darkness. There was no moon outside and it was dark. All he could hear were the waves that whispered. He remembered his children blushing whenever he described darkness to them. He would say, "it's as dark as a sunburnt crow's ass" and they would blush and giggle. He missed them.

He could hear his quadruped friends on the veranda and realized that if it were not for them, he would have really felt lonely. He stubbed out the cigar and rested his sore back. He had walked for miles today. It had been a cloudy day and thus he could walk on the beach till it was late at night. He missed Baba tremendously. It was all very well to know that Baba was with him always but he longed to talk to him, serve him, press his feet, listen to his wisdom and hear jokes about his culinary skill or the lack of it. He missed the old man's aura and energy. Rudra shut his eyes and prayed. Pleaded for the old man to pour his energy into him and erase the heartache and depression slowly building in every cell of his being. After a few moments Rudra sighed. He could sense Baba's energy and presence. He knew the old man was around. Rudra smiled. He was certain Baba smiled back.

All your answers are within son. Not outside. Forget auras and *chakras* and paranormal and new age and pyramids and tarots and channeling and all the fancy words and connect with the most basic word, nothingness and in that nothingness you will find the Creator. He created everything out of nothingness and thus you need to go back to nothingness to reach Him. Crafty Old Man this Creator of ours.

In the morning, Rudra sat on his familiar seat, with a bandana on his head, deep in prayer and meditation. He was aware of how important and crucial the channeling session was to be for the grieving father. He wasn't certain if he would be able to communicate with his son, who had left the physical body, but Rudra wanted to give it his best. That is what the old man would have expected out of him.

"Son, heaven only sees intentions and effort. Success can be karmic. The best of efforts have borne no fruit, simply for the fact that during that phase success was not part of the karmic blueprint. Thus give life your best shot and be in peace with your effort."

So Rudra was going to give all his focus and energy in trying to assuage the grief that had engulfed the very soul of a devastated father. Rudra heard Blondie shuffle outside on the veranda. Rudra shut his eyes and prayed to Baba to fill him up with HIS energy, presence and let only HIS guidance and words pour through and guide and heal the person who sought refuge. Rudra had insisted that Deshmukh too come along, even if it meant, to sit outside and take in the majestic view of the sea and give his quadruped friends company.

Rudra expected to see an old man but Wadhwani could not have been more than forty-seven years of age, with dark hair and a wheat brown complexion that was well taken care of. The moment Rudra looked into his eyes, he saw and even shared, Wadhwani's different states of emotion. The obvious ones being that of depression, anguish, helplessness and frustration but the most powerful sentiment, that virtually overshadowed all other emotions, was that of self-reproach. Rudra had no control over the transference of these emotions from the older man to him. Similarly, emotions such as sadness, anger and impotency as well as over all negativity too were passed on unconsciously from those who came for channeling to the medium. Thus it was a common experience, that most of those who came for channeling, went back light hearted and experienced a sensation of release and optimism, very often leaving the channel weak and distraught. But as the old man had so often warned Rudra, that 'if you want to swim then you should be ready to get wet'.

Rudra inhaled deeply, nodded and motioned the man to be seated. He then shut his eyes and waited for Sai Baba's energy to flow through him. He had learnt that filling himself with Sai Baba's force, allowed Rudra to be a clearer, more accurate and a better medium. Certain times, especially when tired, he had realized that though the message would come through, often Rudra either could not decipher its inherent meaning or the exact words. When the energy was strong, Rudra could virtually see the person's past, present and future as well

Remember, what Avtar Meher Baba, so often says, *God is all Merciful but the path to God is merciless.* My beta, return to simplicity and purity and through them become God itself. Also, remember through meditation and prayer, not only does the individual burn off pending karmas but also they create a shield of protection; either the prayer will ward off the trouble or give the individual strength and wisdom, love and compassion to face whatever is in store with grace, humour and positive acceptance.

as every issue, be it spiritual, emotional, mental or physical, like an open book.

"Baba says that your son is with HIM. Baba says that your son is going through so many conflicting emotions, especially those of disbelief and helplessness and your grief and your dark depressions are making it very hard for your son to move on spiritually."

"What does all that mean? I don't understand?"

"Son, when the soul leaves the physical body, it has certain choices to make. One of the main choices to be made is whether the soul wants to move on with its spiritual journey or wants to be earth-bound. Many times the person refuses to believe that he or she is dead. The person keeps assuming that all that being experienced is a dream or a nightmare and that in a matter of some time, the person will wake up and life will go on as usual. The person is in denial or very often, as the person has never believed in any sort of life after death, the person cannot perceive or acknowledge that he or she is really dead and it is time to move on. Thus the soul keeps hovering around its dead body and hovering around those it loves or hovers around what it is obsessed with. Many times people are so hedonistic and obsessed with material pleasures that they seek to gratify their obsessions through other people and thus you have cases of possession and exorcism. Being earth-bound is a common occurrence with those who have always let the physical world enchant and rule them and not given time for prayer, meditation and spiritual growth. But, sometimes, even though the soul is matured, it still lingers around its loved ones, especially when the person sees the loved ones completely distraught with grief. Let me ask you a simple question. If you knew that your most loved one was unhappy and buried under depression and grief, wouldn't you leave all that you are doing and travel from one part of the earth to the other, just to be with your loved one?"

"Yes."

"The same way, if your loved one who has passed over and left the physical body, realizes that those he or she has left behind, are overwhelmed with grief and are devastated, the soul refuses to move on, but stays by the loved ones. Imagine the frustration and helplessness of the soul, which can see and feel and hear everything but can't be seen or felt or heard. The soul wants to assure its loved ones that it is still around but can't and all the while the soul sees his or her loved ones in grief and devastated. Can you imagine the plight of the soul? Do you really think the soul will want to move on with its spiritual journey? There is something called free will, especially if the soul has reached some sort of spiritual growth. If the soul uses its free will to hover around its loved one, it may hover around for years and years. Do you know what kind of existence that is? That is worse than all of hell put together. You are devastated by the loss of your son. We understand that. But do you have any idea what your grief is doing to your son? It is destroying him further and further every moment and

The easiest way to work out one's karma and clean the slate of karmic dues and protect oneself and one's family is through prayers, meditation, charity and a positive acceptance of all that the Master has in store for you.

the worst part of it all is that he can see and hear everything and he can't do anything about it. Can you imagine the kind of helplessness he is going through? That helplessness leads to frustration, anger and after a while it has a cancerous like effect on the soul."

"I can't help it. I just can't."

"Nobody is telling you not to grieve. Grieving can be a healing process but you are not only just grieving but you have become grief itself; grief to your son and grief to your family who are still living. Your son doesn't exist physically but he exists and will always exist in the spirit plane. You are going to meet him. You do meet him when you sleep. Your higher spiritual body and he connect when you are sleeping but you don't remember anything and can't even feel his presence because your vibrations are clouded by depression and grief and anger and guilt. If you really want to feel him, then let go of all these dark emotions and leave all to God and pray for your son and talk to him and be in peace and you will begin to feel his presence. Then he will move on spiritually but always be around you as and when you think of him or call him to you. It's like picking up a phone and dialing. He will always respond but now you refuse to let him even go out of the room. Do you know what that is doing to his growth?"

"I want to speak to my son."

Rudra shut his eyes and pleaded with Baba to let a grieving father connect in some way with his dead son.

"Ok but for just a short while. Ask?"

"Beta are you ok. My child are you ok?"

Rudra felt the shift in energy. He couldn't describe it but he felt a different energy within him.

"I can't be ok dad, seeing you cry all day. How can I be fine when I see Ma worrying and slowly dying, out of worry for you! I can't."

"Beta, what happened to you? How did you fall off the train?"

"I told you dad, I was very tired. I told you let us not travel by train." Then the words no longer came through but tears formed in Rudra's eyes. He began to feel suffocated. He nearly began to choke. Rudra waited and waited. Then he felt Baba's energy again. "He can't come through. This meeting has overwhelmed him. He needs to rest."

Rudra opened his eyes and saw the father weep quietly. Tears flowed down his cheeks and Rudra, already drained and depressed, felt deep sorrow settle like a dark cloud over his heart. For a long time, the father did not speak. He just sat, eyes open, tears flowing down, while he stared at Sai Baba's original photograph, taken in early 1900s. Sai Baba seated in front of the ever-burning Fire, looking into one's very soul.

"That was my son. He did speak through you. Yes, he did. I have met a number of mediums but only today do I really believe that I have spoken to him."

"Why?"

"Because his last words to me, fifteen minutes before he fell off the train was, 'I am very tired dad so let us travel in a taxi'. These were my son's last words to me before he died and he once again repeated them to me. Please I want to speak to him again. Please!"

Rudra nodded and shut his eyes. But it was of no use. He could sense that the lad was nowhere around. He prayed to Baba to come through.

"Whatever you want to know about your son, ask Me, and I will answer. If you want to really help your son and let his soul be in peace, then you begin to start living in peace. If you begin to live in peace and begin to pick up the pieces of your life, trust me you will be doing the greatest favour to your son. If you really love him, then you make an effort to start living again. I am not telling you to forget your son. I am not telling you to go and party. I am not telling you to start faking happiness. All I am telling you is to begin making an effort to live your life as respectfully and as gracefully as is humanly possible. Yes, you will never forget your son. Yes, you will always ache for him. Yes, there will be times tears will just gush down and your heart will feel as though it is going to burst. That is only human and that is only to be expected. But if you remember that your loved one is still there and can hear you and you are going to meet up, not only after you too leave your physical body but also when you sleep calmly, your grief will be manageable. Keep a time aside everyday, maybe ten minutes, when you call your son, and talk to him. Yes, he may not reply back, but he is hearing you. Pray for your loved one, as prayers have the power of helping souls to grow spiritually. Prayers remove the anger and frustration and impotency that the soul feels and prayers help the soul to grow and evolve and be able to move on with its spiritual journey but that doesn't mean he or she doesn't come to see you. For the soul, all it takes is a pure thought and he or she will be with you. But by constantly grieving, you are chaining your son and your loved one. Don't! Its hell or should I say, its worse than hell. Hell is nothing but a state of mind. Why make your loved one go through such a state of mind, filled with grief, anger and helplessness?"

"I want to know once the train started to move, after how much time did my son fall off the train?"

"You want to test, my son, this child of mine who is my medium and you want to test me too?'

"No..."

"Yes, you do. Your son fell before the train left the station. Your son fell down, nine and a half seconds after the train started. Your son died before he hit the tracks. He died of a heart attack. Your son fell after a stone hit his left eye. The shock and impact of the stone caused a heart attack and he died before his head hit the rails. Check the autopsy report, which you haven't. His left eye had burst from within. He had told you he was tired but you thought the best thing for him was to go by train, as you feared he might be caught up in traffic. It was a genuine fear and you have nothing to feel guilty for. His time of death had come. You aren't responsible for your son's death. Even if you had sent him in a taxi or a plane or not sent him anywhere at all, your son would have still died. Death needs just an excuse and death creates its own excuse. Your wife's prayers and

Complete surrender to the Master is the only way to merge with God Almighty. Give as much as you can; give and give whatever you can give. A poor man might not be able to give much money but he or she can be a decent human being and help family and friends and everyone possible. By being a decent human being you are indulging in the best kind of charity possible.

your family's charity work, has made certain that your son is being taken care of in the spirit plane and that he is with Me. Continue with the prayers and the charity and help as many old people as you can who have lost their young children. Help the orphans and the aged who have nobody to call their own or take care of them. By praying and indulging in charity, you will be really helping your son and helping his spiritual growth and helping your spiritual growth as well. Remember, suicide will make certain that you will never meet your son for a very, very, very long period of time, so don't even think about it. If you kill yourself, you will be your son's worst enemy, as you will make him grieve further and plunge him into anger and doubt and guilt and that will propel him into the depths of the spirit world, where you would not even want your worst enemy to be in. So, if you really love the person who has left the physical world, pray, give in charity and live gracefully. Go now. God be with you."

For an hour, Rudra slept on bed, in a dark room, staring at the flame and SAI Baba's photograph. He felt the man's pain and knew how the man must feel, for Rudra had experienced the man's pain, sorrow and guilt.

Three hours later, Deshmukh arrived with a cell phone, as Wadhwani wanted to talk to Rudra. He had read the autopsy report. Yes, his boy's left eye had burst due to impact. Yes, he had died of a heart attack. Yes, he had died before his head hit the tracks. Yes, he was going to make his son proud of him. Yes, he was going to begin to live once again.

Rudra shut his eyes and thanked GOD for giving him the opportunity of being of some assistance to a grieving father and some relief to a son, who mourned in the spirit plane for the parents he had left behind.

WHILE RUDRA SLEPT, he saw his son and daughter. He could hear them, his son's throaty deep voice and his daughter's laughter. He could smell their baby fragrance and feel their warmth and the wetness of their loud kisses, on his cheeks. He could hear their hearts race and though he slept, tears rolled down and trickled on his neck. He was oblivious to the tears, as even in his sleep, he was weeping with disbelief, that at last he held his children, after years of separation. He felt as though his heart would split wide open, with the contentment of holding and hugging his children. Just being with them, after years. The same children, who had spent virtually every waking moment with him by their side, and he, who had centered his life round them. They were the axis on which his life had revolved. In reality, it still did.

In his dream, they had grown up but still their essence was the same. His son spoke to him, telling him repeatedly, that he missed Rudra every day. Rudra

There is one infallible law of planet earth: there are no free meals; you pay for everything, one way or another. Only with the Master free meals are provided. Only with the Guru can one expect anything without any strings attached. The Master wants nothing from you but that you walk the right path and merge with God.

wanted to tell his boy that a day was too long, to cope; every moment had been a moment too long, too empty, too painful, without him and his sister. Suddenly, his son began to cry and plead with Rudra not to go...

The last thing Rudra remembered, before he sat up with a jerk, was hearing the cry of his son. For a while, he sat, with eyes still shut. The aura of his children, merged with his; their fragrance, their warmth, their kisses, their presence, enveloped his sense of reality; but then his son's cry, from some deep recess of his sub-conscious mind, sent a shiver, through Rudra's spine. The glow of the flame, allowed his tense body to relax and he exhaled and inhaled deeply, as all the while, he had forgotten to breathe. The collar of his shirt was damp. It was a few seconds later that he realized that the dampness was the result of tears that had streamed down his face. His heart hurt. Actually hurt. Any moment, he would not be surprised, to feel his heart explode and put to end years of anguish, isolation, hollowness and the perpetual need to hold and reconnect with his children. His life had become a dark cold abyss where his soul had got trapped in. He felt his eyes brimming with tears. He took a deep breath and sat upright. He wanted to go back to sleep but knew that was wishful thinking. He sighed aloud. He didn't blame anybody. He certainly did not hold anything against anyone. If infidelity was his crime, he wasn't alone in it but he certainly hadn't stooped to the base level of manipulating his children, spreading lies, maligning and indulging in slander. His greatest folly was misplaced compassion and being blind to the true nature of these so-called loved ones and their real worth. Abusing children's growing minds and filling them with hatred and using their innocent childhood to manipulate and seek hollow attention, was something that was not in his temperament. He could live with his cross. He wondered whether those who had so horribly influenced his children, tampered with their fragile minds and hearts, could live with the weight of their cross. It felt strange to be abhorred by his very blood. How could children be so easily brainwashed and convinced to hate their own parent. To hate someone who had loved them more than life and sanity itself.

No matter how hard he tried he couldn't stop his son entering his mind and playing havoc with his emotions. He missed his child. He often wondered how a small child with curly hair could destroy all the composure, tranquility, wisdom, philosophy, and make a grown man weep; a man, who had taken all the badgering life could possibly hand out with a smile; but this boy with curls and dimples and the wettest kiss and the huskiest voice and the warmest embrace, with ease, time and again destroyed all of Rudra's defenses and played havoc with his sanity.

Did his children miss him? Did they think or dream of him? Did they manage to still hold on to the good times (and they sure had many great times). Did his son remember his dad waking him up, carrying him to the

Love the Guru and God like dogs love their master and family. Unconditional. What does the dog want from the master? Nothing but love and its master's presence! It obeys every command.

sofa, giving him his Protinex milk while he continued watching Cartoon Network? Did he remember bath times, then getting dressed, rushing down and zooming on the bike to his tuitions and then off for lunch and then dropping him at school and then Rudra picking him up from school and each night, his son holding Rudra, till he slept? My son, do you remember any of these things or has the hatred, the nonsensical allegations and the scheming, enveloped you too?

He knew his daughter did not miss him. For some reason, beyond his comprehension, she had turned against him. The reason only God would be able to explain. He wasn't sure how he knew but he had heard that she abhorred him. Rudra breathed in deep. How could a child, to whom you have given your best, suddenly begin to hate you? For that matter, Rudra couldn't for the life of him understand how could anybody hate one's very own? How can you hate somebody who, not only has given you pure and selfless love but also asked for nothing else in return? Rudra sighed and stood up. He lit a cigarette, got out of the

The dog will sleep, wait, eat, breathe and condition its entire life to please and be with the master. The dog has no demands but that of love and tenderness. No conditions apply. For the dog the master is never wrong. The master may flog the dog but the dog will wag its tail ten minutes later at the sight of the master. That is pure love. If mankind can love as a dog loves his master than trust me, child, the spiritual kingdom is yours for the asking. Love unconditionally. Love completely. Become love itself.

cottage and began to walk along the beach. His pets walked side by side. It was three in the morning. They wondered why their friend walked so late in the night and why water trickled down his eyes and wet his unshaven cheeks.

A little while later, Rudra got into his black van, made sure his friends were comfortable on the back seat and he drove slowly, with the moon looking down upon him and a sad Leonard Cohen song serenading the night.

RUDRA SLEPT LONG after the sun had begun its journey through the sky. When he woke up, it was mid noon. He stood up, stared at the flame, saw the Masters look at him and for a while, he stared back and then shaking his head in resignation, he walked onto the veranda. They were witness to everything. In spite of it all, if They wished to let him burn and get extinguished with the flame of sadness and the ramifications of false allegations and brutal resentment, so be it. If his Masters, for whatever reason, wanted his children to stay away from him and hate him, so be it. He was too tired, too washed up and virtually no longer consciously part of the living world, to wish for any sort change, anymore. So be it!

The sky, as though sensing his frame of mind, was covered in darkness and it was a matter of moments, before the clouds burst and wept. The monsoons were on their way out and Rudra would miss the rains. He once again wanted to flee the cottage. He once again wanted to be on the move. He had been told often, that his soul was in his feet and thus he never remained in a place for too long. The dogs were there, lazing in the small garden. They saw him and began to wag their tails. Rudra looked at them and managed a smile. They came gamboling towards him, and he patted them and allowed them to love him in their own demonstrative way. He got out the milk and poured it in three separate plastic bowls. He crushed a few biscuits in the milk and also added small pieces of bread. He was aware that Blondie, the brown dog, did not like bread soaked in milk, but preferred eating it dry. So, he kept three slices of bread near the bowl, on the grass. The tails kept wagging at varying degrees of intensity, but they waited patiently till Rudra had prepared and set their breakfast. Rudra had observed Viya, in America, prepare and set meals for his beautiful Golden Retriever, Spens. He had taught Spens to wait till the meal was completely set, in her fancy bowl, and only when he said 'come Spens, eat your food', would she approach the bowl, put her head into it and go 'chomp chomp'. However hungry she was, this ritual never varied.

His three dogs, all curs of varying degrees of strange parentage and breed, somehow learnt fast whatever was taught to them. Normally he would say something like, 'Ok, you sweet bastards...eat up'. But today, he just looked at them, nodded, walked away and sat on the steps of the cottage. Usually, they would rush towards their bowls, but this day, they too sensed the sadness and pain in the man's eyes and they somberly approached their food. Blondie looked at Rudra and only when the man managed a smile and told her to eat, did the animal bow its head into the bowl and eat. Blondie never ate without Rudra's vocal permission. The other two, belonging to the male specie weren't all that particular.

Through the day, Rudra couldn't shake off the dream or the sensation it had stirred in his very soul. It was as though he had really spent time with his kids and experienced their presence, not in state of dreams but in reality. The entire day passed as though in a trance. Fortunately, nobody was scheduled to come for channeling, and all day, Rudra either sat on the veranda or lay on his thin mattress with past and present all merging together; not thinking about his children but they never really leaving him, for a moment.

Where was the Old Man? This time, he had disappeared for nearly a month. He missed the wise sage with his noble presence and restful aura, warm eyes that never judged, words that only healed and jokes that made the child within Rudra laugh.

That night, Rudra once again entered his black van, and slept in it, but kept the doors open, for his three friends, all sprawled, on the grass, a few feet away; but from a spot, where they could all see him. It was as though they realized he was alone, aching and yearning, and wanted to reassure him that they were there for him.

Beyond them, Rudra could see the sand, the white frothy waves and could hear the ocean sing its strange lullaby either to him or to the full moon that bathed the world in her soft luminous silver glow.

Three days later Rudra was back to channeling. Word of mouth, accuracy of prediction and most importantly, being treated with compassion, the absence of being judged or looked down upon and suggesting simple changes to tackle or face serious issues, which brought about relief and hope, made people flock to the small cottage and to the strange man, who looked more like a washed-up hippie but for some odd reason, had his fingers on their pulse, a cure for their burdened minds and a balm for their bruised hearts.

"So, HOW IS my famous child who makes tea that even the heavens fear?"

Rudra prostrated himself and held Baba's feet and tears flowed down and wet Baba's feet. Baba sat down by the young man and caressed his hair.

"Please don't leave me. I don't want anything. No human relationship, no sanity, no peace, not even heaven, just you. Don't leave me and go Baba."

"My silly boy, where can I go, if you don't want me to; I am always with the heart that calls out to me and wants me by his or her side. I cannot leave my children, even if they forget me. Yes, if you want to feel my presence, all the time, then my child you must remember me all the time. That is all I ask. But you, my boy, are always with me. I have eaten every meal with you as you have always offered me the meal first, before putting a morsel in your mouth. I have seen all the fascinating sunrises and sunsets with you, as you asked me to be present with you, each time the sun did its illusionary dance."

"I don't know all this heavy duty spirituality, Baba. I just want you to be with me. Physically and spiritually."

"My boy, physically and spiritually, one must have eyes to see. Most of the time, God is begging to be seen, but is ignored. Life is strange my child, you must not get ensnared by its illusions. Focus more and more on your God and Guru and you shall feel the presence, within and outside you as They have to be present with the disciple; it is mandatory for Them. God and Guru owe it to their children. Just as being upright, kind and noble is a must for the disciple, so God and Guru too are bound by rules of the ancient hermitage, where their presence is mandatory. I am here for a few days in the flesh, to teach you a few things regarding healing. Alas, to pass on to you ancient wisdom of how to make good tea is even beyond this old man who you call Baba."

They had tea with cookies that had been presented to Rudra by one of the numerous families who came for guidance, predictions and counseling. The kitchen was filled with delicacies from all over the world. Some offered flowers, incense and oil. Some cigars. Some cookies. Some cash. Rudra placed all the offerings first before Sai Baba and only then did as he deemed fit. Now he showed all the offerings to Baba. The old sage smiled and blessed Rudra.

"Where is my share of tobacco?"

"Oh, I have kept that in the blue haversack." Rudra got up and handed Baba the haversack, where Rudra had kept Baba's share of cigars and tobacco. Obviously, Baba did not have to be present to know all that which Rudra did.

"If you observe, I have given you more than I have consumed. The last thing I want is to be accused by a cigar smoking sage that I have left him out of the smoking stash."

Baba like a small child went through all the fancy cigars and tobacco and then handed them back to Rudra.

"I am happy with my tobacco. Though don't for a moment think I don't get all that you keep for me. I receive and bless all that you place before me. Sharing what you have with me son, is all that matters to me. Share with me your joys and your pain; your food and your doubts; your cigars and your illusions; your love and your restlessness. I want it all. Don't keep me away from anything. Nothing. I am you and you, my child, are I. Every child is in me and I am in every child. I am the sunrise and the sunset. I am the moon and the waxing and waning of it. I am fire and the light and the heat that comes forth from it. Never, ever, distinguish me separate from matter and mind. I am all. All are Me! I was present in Jesus and Zoroaster and Ram and Meher and Kali, just as THEY are present in me. We are one and in one, we all exist. Fools try to differentiate between us. Fools succeed with fools. Be wise. Can you separate the wave from the ocean? Can the light be separated from the flame? Can you separate the sunbeams from the sun or the fire from its warmth? The fruit comes from the seed and gives seeds to get more fruit. Nature is all encompassing and never differentiates. Only foolish mankind differentiates and tries to prove some nonsensical superiority. Now come, let us take a walk with these three friends of yours."

Baba, Rudra and the three playful dogs, walked towards the setting sun that was just about to cleanse itself in the flaming water.

"REMEMBER, THE FIRST important rule of healing is that only God and Guru heal. Nobody else can heal.

Everybody else is just a channel for healing. You, my son, are just a medium, a piano, through which the divine music flows. You are neither the musician nor the music, just the instrument. But the instrument needs to be in perfect tune and harmony; the strings should be neither too tight nor too loose. Thus, the instrument is very important. Howsoever proficient a musician and however beautiful and melodious the tune, if the instrument is not in perfect condition and tuned up right, the music that flows out of it, shall not be as pleasing as it ought to be. Of course, a Master musician will still bring out amazing music even from a rusted tin but the effort and strain is not worth the while. There are millions of instruments, just a few Master Musicians, thus it is best to keep the instrument in perfect shape.

"Now, just like becoming a channel for predictions and guidance and counseling, each one of us is a channel for healing too. Each one of us! Take your children. I know, when they fell ill, they gravitated towards you and they would sleep on your lap or hold you tight and you would spend all day and night with them. Most often, they felt better immediately, or they felt at least less ill and more comforted. This happens with most children. They may be very ill but the moment their parents, or their loved ones, hold them or are with them, they feel the illness and discomfort ebb. It could happen with one's parents or with elders; maybe grandparents, a Godmother, an elderly maid, spouse, or even just being in one's own protective surrounding; like, being in one's own bedroom or home. Why? The reason is simple, there is subconscious healing taking place. I remember, when your children fell ill, you would hold them close and though you didn't know it, you used to give your own energy to them; allowing them to get stronger and be able to fight the illness that had plagued their small bodies. I know how miserable you were when your children were ill. They may forget. I never shall.

"The Masters and nature, keeps all accounts. No love and emotion goes to waste. We receive everything and preserve it. So, my son who has no inclination to live and all the desire to die, remember, we all are channels and instruments through which the yoke of karma can be erased and settled. That is why it is often observed that when the owner or master of the house is very ill, the pet dog or horse sometimes dies. It is not only because of emotional trauma but also because the pet wants the master to be well and is unconsciously healing the master; giving out his or her energy, trying to fill the master up with its own *prana* and life energy. Why do you think Masters were and are always ill and always suffering from discomfort, pain or illness, all through Their lives. Take any Master and if you ask His or Her disciple, you will be told how unwell the Master is virtually all the time. Why? Because the Master consciously keeps taking on the karma and illnesses of the disciples and devotees and thus illnesses plague spiritual Masters. Take Sai Baba, Meher Baba, Ramakrishna Parmahansa, Raman Maharishi, Kamu Baba, all of Them were ill; all of Them throughout Their lives suffered for the karma and ill health of their disciples. It's not that They could not cure Themselves, They could, but there are certain laws of energy and karma and They abided by those laws. If Jesus wasn't ready to be crucified, do you really believe any man on earth or any force in the Universe could have managed to touch a hair on His head, leave aside make Him wear a crown of thorns or crucify Him? No. He allowed it to happen. He wanted to take on the cumulative karma of mankind. He took these on to Himself and thus allowed Himself to go through pain-agony-abuse that only Masters can go through for their children. And all this made all the more painful, for the Master can stop or shield Himself from feeling pain, but He doesn't, as that interferes with His plan and the law of karma.

"Remember, the law of nature works in simple ways; somebody has to absorb whatever energy is set loose. Somebody has to foot the bill. Whether the individual pays or the Master, the law of nature and karma is not really interested. Same system operates with healing and the karma of pain and illness. As I have mentioned, somebody has to foot the cosmic bill. There are no free meals in the cosmos. Thus, when Gurus and Masters or even channels of healing, go about their task of working with energy and karma, somebody has to pay for their actions. Energy and karma only want to know, 'where do I go now?' To whom they go, can be negotiated; the energy or karma network can be convinced to overlook the person, but it has to go someplace. You cannot destroy matter; only change its form. Same way you cannot obliterate somebody else's karma, but only transfer it. The Master may not want His or Her disciple to suffer from cancer. But karmically, the person has to experience cancer and all that which comes along with the disease. The Master knows best. The Master decides that the 'child' should no longer suffer from the illness. The disciple should be cured. Up to this point, there is no problem with the cosmos. The karmic accountant can be convinced to change the address of billing but the bill has to be sent and paid for; somebody has to foot the bill. The karma has to be worked upon. They don't mind the energy of cancer removed from the individual but the energy needs to be accounted for and worked upon. It needs to be given a decent burial. It can't be kept floating in the karmic cosmos. It needs to be laid to completion. The energy automatically gravitates to the person, who is the cause of its uncompleted mission. It seeks a home. It gravitates to the person who has been the cause of its homelessness. It abides in the Master or the channel. Now the Master soaks in the karmic leftovers and the Master goes through the pain and agony, but due to His or Her spiritual strength, the Master works out the energy of the karma in a very short while. But the pain is all the more excruciating as the Master works out the karma in a few days. All that which the illness was to achieve and teach the Master takes on and digests in a few days time. You can imagine the pain. Excruciating. That is the karma of just one disciple. The Master has thousands or millions.

"All this give and take of karma eventually saps the Master and the health of the Master starts to get ruined but the Master continues soaking in the karmas' of the disciples. That is why we say the Guru comes before God. God has laid down the laws and thus God too is bound by those very laws and remember God is all Just. God cannot be lenient to some and unsparing to others; unless the case is presented by the Guru. When the Guru seeks for karmas to be changed or altered, God consents.

The Guru is like a mother; all merciful and with a heart that beats and bleeds for the disciples. The Master thus bends the laws for the peace and happiness of the disciples; but the Guru pays the price that is so excruciating that nobody can decipher or comprehend. Remember, there are no healers. Only God and Master are Healers; everybody else are just channels for healing. Never ever call yourself a healer. Always call yourself a channel for healing. It is not only the modest thing to say but also the right thing to say.

"The problem starts with those who are not Masters but are destined or really yearn to become channels of healing. As they are not Masters, they do not have the capacity to digest the workings of karma and displaced energy but as they are channels for healing, they have the power to initiate the transference of energy and karma. They can remove the illness; they can work on the karma and energy pattern, but after that comes the real issue. Energy demands its pound of flesh, and it gravitates towards the channel. The problem starts here. Does the channel have the power to shield his or her aura and body? Is the armour of humility, detachment and a state of egoless protective covering able to protect him or her from the transfer of energy and divert the energy to the Cosmic River, the Master? The Master is one with God, thus the Master and God have become one and are one entity; remember, the ocean and wave are one and yet separate. The Master, through the disciple's effort, achieves the transfer of karma and energy and then takes it upon Him or Herself; but this transfer is only possible if the disciple first of all is completely in tune with the Master; is an empty instrument; is strong to absorb the energy transfer and hasn't brought his or her ego into the picture.

"If the channel of healing hasn't taken the right steps of protection and hasn't taken the right steps of detachment and hasn't achieved an egoless state, then the real problems start. The transfer of the illness, from the patient to the Cosmic River doesn't take place. It's something like a bank. In electronic banking terms, the transfer hasn't reached the right account. There is a problem in the connectivity and the funds remain in the place of origin of deposit. Remember, the funds have already been deposited in the karmic account of the channel, awaiting a transfer to the karmic vault of the Master; but if the transfer is not affected, then the channel for healing has to start paying interest from his own pocket. The patient or the client has deposited the illness or the amount, which logically was to be sent to the Master, but the transfer hasn't taken place and every second the transfer is delayed, the interest accumulates. Sometimes, the amount deposited is so high that the channel cannot afford to pay the interest, leave aside the full sum. Thus, the channel for healing should make sure the transfer is done immediately with no residue left behind. The Bank of karma has stringent rules. Kings have become paupers. Only when you are sure of the transfer facilities and only when you are sure that your connection with the Master Vault is working perfectly, should one open an account of healing. Now, more about healing later on, for even in my karmic blueprint, I have grief, pain and indigestion destined. Punish me with your food. Ha! Ha!"

"Ok my Hilarious Sage."

The sun had set a while back but darkness still waited on the horizon with her black blanket. The two men and their three friends walked towards the cottage. It had rained last night but now it was quite apparent that summer had begun to make her passionate presence felt with her warm embrace. Somewhere, a radio played out an old Hindi film tune. Rudra would have been engulfed with depression and thoughts about his children, but not today. Today, he had his father, old friend and sage with him. Today, he would sleep well. He would sleep without dreams.

TWO WEEKS LATER Baba left and as though on cue, people started coming over with illnesses. Baba had taught Rudra how to become a channel of healing.

"Remember whether you are a medium for healing or you are praying for somebody's health, the most important point to be remembered is that you need to have body, mind and heart all moving in the same direction and without any attachment or passion. No conflict. Secondly, you must not be in a state of ill health of any sort. Remember, you are not a Master but a medium and thus your body cannot absorb too much of negative energy. If you are not in the right health or frame of mind, it means the chances of negativity enveloping you and seeping within you and clouding your aura are very high and thus, though you may be instrumental in the healing process of another, you will absorb the person's illness and fall ill. The problem is that by the time you fall ill, you will have absorbed so much negativity and illness that the very life force within you will be nearly extinguished. If the fire within you starts flickering and is almost extinguished, your body, mind and aura will succumb to ill health, restlessness, negativity, lethargy and all the dark emotions. Thus, first and foremost you need to be healthy; body, mind, heart and soul. If you feel you are well, then you need to first sit in meditation and prayer. Always do healing in front of the fire– oil lamp and incense sticks and camphor are also fine. I have taught you the prayer. This prayer should be prayed whether you are a medium or just saying a prayer for somebody ill. *Fill my body, mind and soul; auras, vibrations and channels; every drop of blood, DNA and cell; my entire being, with your protection, love, guidance, strength, healing energies, spiritual energies and grace; forgive me, lead me, guide me, guard me and have mercy on me.*

"Then you say the most important prayer for healing. Remember, though illness may be self-created but often it is karmic. If it is karmic, your trying to work on the person's ill-health means you are tampering with the individual's karmic blueprint. Maybe nature wants the individual to go through the illness and now, you want to release the individual from the experience and illness and discomfort. Maybe the illness is a very prominent learning curve for the individual. Now no matter what you may do, the individual will not be cured and this will only lead to further frustration, doubt and anxiety in both the individual and yourself. So it is important that you add a small prayer after the initial prayer. Pray that: *please use me as a medium to heal this child of yours. Let only your energy and grace flow through me to heal this child of yours. Please heal this child's body, mind and soul; auras, vibrations, channel; every drop of blood, DNA and cell but If for whatever reason the child has to go through the illness and the experience of the illness, please give the child, wisdom, strength, love and compassion to go through the illness and experience with grace, positive surrender and even happiness.*

"This is an important prayer as what you are telling the Cosmos is, if the illness is self-created and can be cured, do so; but if for whatever reason, the person has to go through the illness, let the person go through it with grace and positive surrender. Thus, though the illness may prevail, the individual will begin to feel better, mentally, emotionally, spiritually and be able to cope with the physical discomfort in a much calmer manner."

The first patient that came to Rudra was a fifty-five year old man. He worked as a cashier in a departmental store twenty kilometers away. He had heard of Rudra from his driver. The driver's daughter had gone missing. Through channeling, Baba had told the grieving father that his daughter would be back next day by noon. She was well but upset with him. Baba also told the father not to be such a tyrant. Children are like flowers. One needed to handle them with love, care and yet firmness; but not like a bull in a china shop. The man had asked what the hell was a china shop. The daughter returned home at eleven-thirty the next day. Both, the father and daughter visited Rudra in the evening and presented him with the most delicious homemade chips. So, this fifty-five year man, called Hosi, a Zoroastrian, came into the cottage. Rudra sat down for channeling from forenoon till sunset. Of course, he usually spent the entire morning in predictions and healing sessions too, but the official time was four. Nobody took the official time very seriously, including Rudra. People dropped in whenever they liked.

Hosi wasn't much of a believer. He looked at Rudra and it was obvious he didn't like Rudra's hippie look too well. But Hosi had travelled a long way, and he now cursed Mukesh, his driver, the silly sod, who had gone on and on about this crazy looking man with long hair and a bandanna around his head.

Rudra said his prayers and then shut his eyes and prayed to Baba. Then Rudra placed his right palm over Hosi's left palm. The palms did not touch. There was a gap of an inch or maybe more. Rudra shut his eyes and after a while Hosi began to feel heat in the center of his left palm. Initially, it was just a prickling sensation that grew warm and then hot.

"I feel suffocation. I feel breathless. I am feeling giddy. The world's moving in circles. All this because you just don't know how to breathe."

Then Rudra opened his eyes and put his hand down.

"I have a feeling your problem is that you just don't breathe properly."

Hosi looked as though any moment he would punch Rudra hard on the nose.

"Look here, you are trying to tell me, the main cause of my ill-health is that I don't breathe properly."

"I am trying to tell you that the core reason for your ill-health is that you don't breathe properly. I am not a doctor thus may not be able to give you a medical name for your problem but you not breathing well and that is the cause of your illness."

"Look here. I respect what you are doing for the

poor and the ill but let me tell you something. I have been suffering from fainting spells for the past twenty years. I have tried every known cure and every known treatment. I have gone to Canada and got my tests done and met every known doctor who could have helped me. I have spent a fortune and more and now you are telling me that I keep fainting and getting convulsions and black-outs because I don't know how to breathe."

Rudra took a deep breath. He was new to all this. He was aware that he had no rational explanation. He was also certain that while feeling the person's energy and vibration, he had felt suffocation, giddiness and nausea. The man obviously had done his work and been treated by a truckload of fancy doctors. Oh Baba! Then suddenly, a warm sensation entered Rudra. His breathing got more regular. A certain confidence and power filled his being. Rudra smiled. He knew the Old Man was around.

"Yes. You are fainting because you aren't breathing properly. Your level of stress is very high and your response to stress is you stop breathing and you breathe very shallowly and thus you faint."

"Look here this isn't logical..."

"Your being here isn't logical too. You think your coming to me is a logical or a rational step? This channeling and all this paranormal stuff is the most illogical thing going around. You don't need to be a rocket scientist to tell me that all this isn't logical. You think people come here for my wisdom and logic? You have come here because you have no place else to go. My reading is that you don't breathe properly. Start breathing deeply. Start focusing on your breath. When you are stressed, shut your eyes and take deep breaths.

This is my advice to you. If it doesn't work, you haven't wasted any money, just a little time and what is time but a state of mind. Now do yourself a favour and breathe. If you do so, I don't think you will faint again. And if you do faint, it will be because you aren't breathing."

The man looked at Rudra for a while and then smiled.

"You are an odd egg aren't you?"

"The oddest egg around my friend. But the fact is that most often solutions are in front of us. We just refuse to acknowledge them."

Three weeks later, Hosi walked through Rudra's door. Nobody bothered to knock any more. They just took it for granted that Rudra would be more than happy to see them all. Very often Rudra was.

"You know what, you crazy man, I haven't fainted yet. First time in twenty years, I haven't fainted in a fortnight. Yes, a week back when I had gone to the chemist, I began to feel faint but I walked out and began to breathe in deep and though everyone around thought I was just another mad Parsi, I became all right."

"JAI BABA (Praise be to BABA). So you are breathing properly?"

"Oh yes and that's thanks to you. I have a friend who works with me in the same office. His name is Rudra too. Whenever I see him or somebody mentions his name, I begin to breathe properly, remembering you," saying this he began to laugh aloud. "Come, let's go and have a drink. There is this café where the staff have been brought in from the Gestapo but the food and beer are great."

Rudra smiled. Yeah, he knew this place only too well.

THE FIRST TIME Rudra realized the power of healing was when a mother and a child entered the room, not for healing but for channeling. The first statement Baba made was about the child's ill health and the need to protect the child from any chest congestion. Rudra answered all the questions but as time went by he began to hear the child's wheezing chest. He mentioned this to the mother. The mother put her ear to the boy's chest.

"I can't hear the wheezing but he has been suffering from chest congestion and asthma since birth."

Rudra looked at the boy. He breathed in deep. The boy was his son's age. He looked at the boy and remembered his son. He didn't want his son or this boy ill; ever.

Two hours later Rudra was down with high fever and his chest was congested and every breath hurt. He knew what had transpired. He had got emotional. He had let his guard down. He wanted the child healed as the child reminded him of his son. By night Rudra was in bad shape. He was coughing hard and his body shivered. He couldn't breathe. It took two days for Rudra to get slightly better and a week to get completely cured. Ten days later the mother and the boy came to meet Rudra. They had brought with them various gifts.

"Thank you." The mother looked at Rudra and the man smiled. "That night, after we met you, after years, my son went to sleep without any medicine or the inhaler. It's been more than a week that he hasn't fallen sick. I know you have taken the illness upon yourself. God bless you."

Rudra smiled. He looked at the boy and patted his silky hair.

"Don't worry about this boy. Baba and my prayers are always with him." Rudra could feel his eyes get wet. He breathed in deep and watched the mother and son walk to their car and drive away. The boy looked back at Rudra till the car disappeared. Of one thing Rudra was certain. If more children visited him for either channeling or healing, he was in for some serious trouble, as there was no way he could detach himself from a child's ill health or plight.

A LOT OF people came for healing. Some went back cured. All of them went back feeling better. During the sessions of healing, Rudra not only gained a glimpse of the root cause of the illness but also into the individual's mind; their fears and aspirations; their past, present and future. This scared the daylights out of many and brought in more people to be healed.

It would be wrong to say that all benefited. It would also be false to say that every prediction of his came true. Often Rudra had to force himself to sit down, even though ill, tired or depressed or Rudra got emotional about the problems being faced by families and it was during such times, when the complete connection didn't take place.

"Beta, the energy can never be wrong. The energy within you will always be accurate. It is within you and will always guide you properly. But, if you let your emotions cloud the passage that the power needs to flow through, then problems and miscalculations can take place. That is why it is of utmost importance that you are in the state of nothingness. This state of nothingness is a must, to allow the energy to pass through unobstructed or manipulated. If obstruction takes place, the energy is so sensitive that it can show you images that your mind will read wrongly and then transmit messages that are different from the source. There is a difference of just one alphabet between the words, 'fate' and 'hate', but a difference of life and death, heaven and hell, between the two words. If you are not in the state of nothingness, the energy will be tampered with and at those moments, mistakes might take place. You will not be able to translate accurately what your sixth sense is trying to tell you or what Baba is trying to say to you. The words come through a tunnel son and you need to be really hear well to understand what each vibration is trying to tell you.

"Son, we are dealing with energy where a single mistake can destroy the individual and the family and cause grief and anguish to those who seek counsel. One mistake from the medium and those who come to seek, instead of going back with the cure, take a deadlier disease back with them. One mistake, a single lapse of concentration, a momentary lapse from the state of nothingness, and you can single-handedly finish that individual or the family or even an entire community. Imagine telling a businessman to expand his operations when actually he should be doing the very opposite. Imagine the man putting up another factory. The factory is fated to shut down. Can you imagine the number of families that will suffer? Not only those who have been newly employed but due to one miscalculation, the individual might have to shut down all his old business establishments too. Can you imagine that a moment's lapse of focus and you can be instrumental in destroying hundreds of families? Forget about what it does to the medium's karmic blueprint. Can you image the grief the medium has directly and indirectly caused? So son, being a medium comes with great responsibility. Always respect and remember the responsibility that you shoulder."

Rudra soon realized that though folks came to him for prediction and healing, in reality, their Masters or Baba, took them into their fold and made them move towards the path of spirituality and charity. Often, those who now had become regulars informed Rudra how after sitting for channeling or healing, their way of thinking and their lives had changed for the better. It wasn't as though all their problems had ceased to exist or life had suddenly become a bed of roses, no, in fact very often, life had become harder but they were better equipped to face the travails of life and also they could handle adversity and trial with more grace and even happiness. But the deciding difference in their life was that they had begun to spend more of their incomes to help the poor, the needy, the abandoned and the sick. They had also begun to feed the hungry–mankind, animals and birds. Many good people had also begun to provide clothes, medicines, shelter, money and even jobs, to the needy. Nothing gave Rudra more happiness than to know that the poor were being taken care of and those indulging in charity were working on their karma too. It was a win-win situation for all. Why don't people realize that when they give in charity or help others in need, they are helping themselves the most? The cosmos took care of you tenfold more when you took care of its poor and the needy. As Baba often said, "Give Providence a reason to help you and the best way is to convince the Universe that you are going to take care of the needy and the sick and hungry and the damned". So many of Rudra's extended family had begun to keep a certain percentage of their earnings to give back to the universe by helping those who needed it the most. One is never too poor to help out. Give according to your capacity, was all Rudra insisted. Take care of your family but remember to take care of God's poor family too.

Rudra also understood one thing very clearly. It was as though whoever the Master really loved went through greater suffering and anguish. Those who the Master had chosen as His very own, and the Master wanted to clear their karmic account, or cleanse the person off the karmic baggage, or to complete the person's karmic balance sheet and keep the child with the Master in the spirit plane were the ones who went through the greatest hardship and obstacles.

"My boy, who can make the heaven cringe with his cooking, the fact of the matter is that to get the purest gold, one needs to put it through more intense fire. You can't get the best quality gold through any other manner. To drink pure water, you have to boil all hell out of it first, my boy. I am sure that isn't a very comforting process. Everything needs to go through its own fire to come out pure and cleansed. Imagine two children playing in the dirt and both have hurt themselves. Imagine, the mother of one of the children, making certain that her child is cleaned up with hot water and soap and then wherever the child is hurt, antiseptic is applied. Yes, for sure, it is going to hurt the child. The child is going to scream in pain and cry in agony. The child is going to maybe even scream at his mother or even abuse everybody around him. Imagine, the child seeing his friend, still playing in the dirt, enjoying himself and nobody insisting that he take a bath and nobody forcing antiseptic on him. You tell me my son, who is better off? The child being forced to get cleaned and have antiseptic dabbed on his wounds or the latter, who still plays about in the dirt and has nobody applying antiseptic on his wounds? When the Master wants to get a child home, the child has to be cleaned up first, antiseptic applied to the wounds; injections given if necessary; medicines to be swallowed if required. Anyway, it is because the Master loves the child and feels that the child needs to now live at home, that the Master goes through all the trouble of cleaning the child. Often, the child longs to go back to the street and often the child thinks his Mother hates him or is not as good as his friend's mother who allows his friend to continue playing in the dirt and not apply any medicine to the wounds. Yes, often that is the case but the Mother doesn't care about all this. Putting a stone on her heart the mother tends to her child's wounds and makes certain the child is safe from further harm. Thus, those who go through a harrowing time, often look heavenward and blame their Master or God for forsaking them, saying 'why me?', when in reality, they must understand that they are being loved and tended and cleansed. And if only they go through the process of cleansing with the knowledge that their Master loves them so much that the Master wants to clean them off all the muck and dirt and bring them closer to Him/Her, trust me, life will change and life will become worth living.

"All answers are within each individual. All the individual needs to do is sit silently and go within. Focus on one's breath and slowly begin the journey back to one's real home. For that, one needs no medium, no ashram, no books, no pseudo master, just faith that your real Master is within you and is eager to guide you back home. Sit quietly and shut your eyes and let go of all thoughts and slowly focus your mind on your breathing and slowly you will realize that you have become your breath itself and then through your breath you have entered the zone where serenity, solitude, spirituality, sages and seers all prevail. All your answers are within son. Not outside. Forget auras and *chakras* and paranormal and new age and pyramids and tarots and channeling and all the fancy words and connect with the most basic word, nothingness and in that nothingness you will find the Creator. He created everything out of nothingness and thus you need to go back to nothingness to reach Him. Crafty Old Man this Creator of ours, who has layered everything that is pure with an illusionary glitter of nonsense that we all get sucked into so that we take our time reaching the state of nothingness. Why? Simple. If you create a puzzle, you will want to make sure that it is the most complex puzzle to crack and that is what our Good Old Man has done. But its complexity is in the fact that actually it is the simplest puzzle to solve but we take every route and every step which takes us away from simplicity and into the web of complexity and thus further and further away from the answer. As Parmahansa Yoganda says *God is simple all else is complex*.

"Remember, what Avtar Meher Baba, so often says, *God is all Merciful but the path to God is merciless*. My beta, return to simplicity and purity and through them become God itself. Also remember, through meditation and prayer not only does the individual burn off pending karmas but also they create a shield of protection—either the prayer will ward off the trouble or give the individual strength and wisdom, love and compassion to face whatever is in store with grace, humour and positive acceptance. The best thing an individual can do with life is pray, meditate, be pure, tender and kind and indulge in lots of charity. The easiest way to work out one's karma and clean the slate of karmic dues and protect oneself and one's family is through prayers, meditation and a positive acceptance of all that the Master has in store for you. Complete surrender to the Master is the only way to merge with God Almighty. Give as much as you can; give and give whatever you can give. A poor man might not be able to give much money but he or she can be a decent human being and help family and friends and everyone possible. By being a decent human being you are indulging in the best kind of charity possible."

NINE WEEKS PASSED. It was mid January. Winter had slowly begun to make her cold presence felt. The mornings and nights were pleasant while the afternoons were still humid and hot. Rudra slept on the veranda sofa and looked out at the night sky. Countless stars glittered and somewhere an insomniac cricket made a nuisance of itself. The dogs lay about on the veranda after a dinner of boiled vegetables and chicken stock with a few bones thrown in to complete the feast. Rudra cooked for them twice a week and stocked the food in the freezer. Feeding them made him feel closer to his children. He shut his eyes and moaned. He was in rather bad shape. His body ached. His breathing was shallow and his head hurt. The pain in his head was worse and his energy level was virtually non-existent. He knew that in a matter of weeks he would be dead. He could sense time closing up on him. He remembered, as a child, having a sand clock. At least that is what everybody insisted on calling the timepiece. It took exactly fifteen minutes for the sand to empty itself into another similar bowl below. Rudra would time his work through that. Four rounds meant an hour and usually Rudra would work for an hour and a half, as he would forget to turn the sand clock once the sand had run itself out. Rudra was certain that his sand was running out too. He could feel it in his bones. He could sense it in his breathing. The cold embrace of death had begun to envelope him. Rudra smiled. All his life he had wanted to die but now that he lay dying, he didn't want to leave mother earth. Or may be he didn't want to leave so soon. Rudra smiled. Even smiling was painful now. He knew this phase would pass and he would gather his strength and again sit for channeling and be an instrument for healing. Where the strength came from or why he forced himself to sit and pray or channel, he had no clue. It was as though he was programmed and he was on auto and he had little option but to go with the flow and follow what ever the programme wanted him to do.

He sighed and sat up on the sofa. He had blisters in his mouth, tongue and way into his throat. For the past three days he had eaten no food and could barely drink water. Even breathing hurt. Since he became to be a medium for healing, apart from his will, every pore and cell in his body ached and felt bruised. He often joked with his dogs that the pain originated from his ass and went through his head. People came from far and they came in carloads. Word of mouth and because pain-agony-helplessness is so universal and so profuse, that mankind will resort to anything and anybody to find a way out of their drudgery, the knots of karma and the stringent settling of scores of the stars above. Rudra was under no illusion that people came because of his so-called powers. Yes, Rudra had been told by innumerable people that their lives had changed due to his presence and his prayers and guidance and predictions. But Rudra brushed all this aside. He was doing nothing but what Baba wanted to be done and he had no illusions about himself. Also, he was aware that one wrong prediction and those who now believed in him would swear at him. Mankind was a strange amalgam of petty emotions and a melting pot of heaven and hell. What rose from that melting pot even the good Lord had to work hard to keep track of. Rudra was also aware that people weren't interested in his health or wellbeing. As long as he could be a medium they would come to him even if he were on his deathbed. But Rudra did not mind or hold this against them. He was aware of human emotions and insecurities and he understood mankind. For some reason he loved mankind. Maybe he himself had so many flaws and weaknesses and issues that he understood and identified with everybody else.

There is one infallible law of planet earth: there are no free meals; you pay for everything, one way or another. Rudra smiled. Only with the Master free meals are provided. Only with the Guru can one expect anything without any strings attached. The Master wants nothing from you but that you walk the right path and merge with God and He or She is aware that there will be innumerable slips and mess ups, innumerable times and life times before the child gets his or her act together and walks on the straight road. Till then the Guru is with the child. Not wanting anything but the good and final home coming of the child. Once when Rudra had asked Baba about how should one's love for the Guru and God be, Baba had replied:

"Love the Guru and God like dogs love their master and family. Unconditional. What does the dog want from the master? Nothing but love and its master's presence! It obeys every command. The dog lives for a smile and a hug. The owner may be rich or may be the poorest

However strong the chariot may be or skilled the charioteer, till all the horses are not in unison about the path and the way through it, only hell and pandemonium rule. Nothing reigns but chaos. Living in the present moment and chanting the Holy Name and walking with the Lord creates, a single- minded desire and a harmonious momentum that makes the journey blissful and enjoyable person on earth or may have from a king turned into a pauper; he or she may be famous or the most condemned person in the universe, but the dog will love unconditionally. The dog will sleep, wait, eat, breathe and condition its entire life to please and be with the master. The dog has no demands but that of love and tenderness. No conditions apply. For the dog the master is never wrong. The master may flog the dog but the dog will wag its tail ten minutes later at the sight of the master. That is pure love. If mankind can love as a dog loves his master than trust me, child, the spiritual kingdom is yours for the asking. Love unconditionally. Love completely. Become love itself. Your dog will live for you and die for you. Its eyes will follow you wherever you go and its eyes will wait for you when you aren't home. It wants nothing in return but your love. That is how one needs to love. Dogs were created to teach mankind how to love and be faithful. Unfortunately, instead of man learning from the dog, nowadays dogs are becoming more like human beings. Sad are the ways of the world."

Two nights later, Rudra lay in his room, moaning in pain. His head felt as though a hot rod had found its way through it. He could not breathe, as even that hurt. His throat from within was filled with blisters as was his mouth and tongue. He hadn't eaten for days. The only consolation about not eating was that he didn't have to wash the vessels. He smiled. *Rudra you've got your priorities all scrambled up brother!* He could hear his friends outside on the veranda. He made a Herculean effort and stood up. Slowly, he navigated his way to the kitchen. Fortunately, there was a bowl with food for them. The last bowl though, he sighed. Tomorrow, what would the SOBs eat? He barely had the strength to walk from one room to another. Going to the market seemed out of the question. But he would have to. *Baba this is a SOS. Give me strength or find somebody else to take care of these friends of mine, as my dear father these three dogs aren't interested in channeling and healing and energy transfer but just love, care and FOOD!* Rudra smiled. He was certain Baba had heard him.

The aroma of the food hurt his stomach. He so desperately wanted to eat but he could not. Rudra slowly went to the veranda. There was instant wagging of tails and whining and even barks of happiness. Rudra saw his friends and tears welled his eyes. He poured the food in their three respective bowls and then slowly buckled on to the sofa. Blondie, as usual waited for Rudra to tell her to begin eating. Rudra could not as he couldn't speak. Blondie waited. Rudra whispered but no audible words came out of his mouth. Rudra signaled Blondie to eat. Blondie waited. Rudra with every last ounce of strength in his body, got up, dragged himself to the bowl, crouched, put his hand in the food, took a morsel and fed Blondie.

Blondie ate the morsel and looked deep into Rudra's eyes. Tears began to stream down the man's unshaven cheeks. Rudra looked into the food, took another morsel and fed his friend. Then he sat by the bowl and motioned Blondie to start eating. After much hesitation, Blondie slowly began to eat. It was obvious that she didn't have the heart either in the food or in the act of eating itself. The other two, finished their meal and sat by Rudra. For a long while all of them sat on the veranda watching the sky and hearing the waves sing their soothing lullaby. The air had a nip to it and Rudra stood up, entered the room, rummaged through his meagre belongings, got out three bed sheets and placed them on the spot where each dog had its territorial hold. Blondie walked towards Rudra. She rubbed her body gently along Rudra's legs. Rudra sighed and slowly made his way back into his room, where the oil lamps burnt and Baba's vibrations were all around.

He slowly got into bed and shut his eyes. He had no idea whether he slept or not. He had no idea whether it was night or day. He knew his time had come. He missed his children. He yearned for them. He remembered all at home. His family. His childhood. His friends. The fun he and his kids had together, in the eleven years they had spent together. He remembered his loved ones. The women he had loved and the women who had loved him so dearly. He had hurt so many but he never meant to. He remembered all, who, in their own wonderful and tender way had enriched his life. Strangely, he never remembered the hate and anger. He could only remember each one of them with love and remember their love for him. He remembered all those who had come for channeling and healing and a soft prayer went out to Baba to take care of them. All those he knew in this lifetime and past life times; all those in the physical plane and in the spirit plane and those in between. Rudra prayed for them all.

Then Rudra saw Baba enter. Baba looked at him and smiled. Baba sat by his side and caressed Rudra's forehead. Rudra wanted to get up to touch Baba's feet but he couldn't. He wanted to tell Baba he really loved him but no words came through. The last image was that of Baba smiling at him and Rudra smiled back.

"You have to die my son to live for ever. Sleep now my beta. When you wake up all will be well, believe in what your Fakir says."

A sigh escaped Rudra's parched lips. He had Baba with him. He wanted nothing more, nothing less. He looked deep into Baba's eyes and slowly darkness enveloped him.

A few seconds later, his three pets entered the room, followed by a young couple. The dogs silently sat near Baba. The young couple saw Rudra lying on bed. They saw three dogs gazing at Rudra. The young couple had never seen him look so peaceful. Something about Rudra made both of them touch Rudra's feet. The young couple looked around the sparse room. Apart from the flames burning bright and Rudra's three friends, there was nobody else in the room, but for some reason, both, man and woman, felt divine eyes observe them. They looked once again at the sleeping man and silently left the room.

Baba looked at the three dogs. He smiled. Tails began to wag incessantly.

Other works by the author